C B Radio 〜〜〜〜〜〜

C B Radio

by Leo G. Sands ~~~~~

South Brunswick and New York: A. S. Barnes and Company
London: Thomas Yoseloff Ltd

© 1960 by Ziff Davis Publishing Company
© 1970 by A. S. Barnes and Co., Inc.
Library of Congress Catalogue Card Number: 69–15774

A. S. Barnes and Co., Inc.
Cranbury, New Jersey 08512

Thomas Yoseloff Ltd
108 New Bond Street
London W1Y OQX, England

SBN: 498 07519 2
Printed in the United States of America

CONTENTS

PREFACE

Ever since police departments started using two-way radiotelephones, there has been a growing interest on the part of the general
public in the use of radio for direct voice communications. One
such use has been the convenience of marine radiotelephones on
pleasure boats; another, mobile telephones installed in cars, which
literally extends telephone service to the automobile.

Today, about four million vehicles are equipped with two-way
radiotelephones for private communications. The taxi cab is dis-
patched to pick up another fare before it returns to home base;
the passenger train engineer is told why the signal light ahead is
red and why he will be ordered to take another track to bypass
a grade-crossing accident; a police sergeant is given an urgent
message concerning a homicide; a TV repairman is told to hurry to
your home to fix the TV set in time for you to see a favorite program; the parcel delivery man saves a trip when he is instructed to
stop enroute to pick up exchange merchandise; the fork-lift truck
operator in a TV plant is told where he can find the green port-
ables stored; and the doctor is summoned while on the road to
make an emergency call.

The air lanes are busy with two-way radio messages. And now,
thanks to Citizens Radio, Mr. Jones can tell his wife when he is
stuck in a traffic jam to tell her that he will be late for dinner;
Mr. Smith can call his family while he is fishing out on the lake
to advise that he weathered the thunder squall without harm; the
newspaper dealer can call the missed paper-delivery car to be sure
to leave the *Times* at the Doe home; the used-car dealer can keep
in touch with the used-car lot down the street; the Blank Company
can have interoffice communication between many of its offices and
buildings without having to install a lot of wiring; the summer
camp on the island need no longer be out of touch with the world;
and the officials at the regatta can keep in touch with each other . . .

thanks to Citizens Radio, which is available to all United States citizens over 18 years of age and which is now within the average person's means.

This book tells the entire story about one important class of Citizens Radio operation—Class D. We have tried to tell just what the Citizens Radio service is and to give an idea of some of its many applications. Transmitting and receiving equipment is discussed in detail and many illustrative circuits are shown. Information on simple installation and maintenance techniques is also included. The material covered is intended to be of interest both to laymen who have use for Citizens Radio equipment and to technicians who want to know more about it.

The author wishes to express his appreciation to the many equipment manufacturers and individuals who so willingly provided information and illustrations for use in this book. Included among these are Earl Broihier of the Heath Company, Jules Rubin of Allied Radio Corporation, Abe Pletman of Lafayette Radio-Electronics Corp., E. F. Johnson Company, The Antenna Specialists Company, International Crystal Manufacturing Company, Frank Genochio of Kaar Electronics Corporation and the Federal Communications Commission.

LEO G. SANDS

New York City

C B Radio ～～～～～

1

WHAT IS CITIZENS RADIO?

Any United States citizen over 18 years of age is eligible to apply for a CRS radio-station license that authorizes the installation and operation of a private two-way radiotelephone communications system. A Citizens Radio communications system may be used for transacting any lawful kind of business or for personal convenience. It may not be used for broadcasting music or other program material. It enables the public to talk by radio [as radio amateurs (hams) have been able to do for almost half a century] without having to pass a code test and a written technical examination, as is required of hams. But, unwarranted communications with unknown persons, in ham style, are prohibited.

A citizen may equip his car, boat, plane, or any other vehicle with a two-way radiotelephone as well as his home, office, or summer cottage. He can own and operate as many Citizens Radio stations as he can afford. He can buy his equipment ready-made or in kit form; or he can lease the equipment.

A Citizens Radio station may be used for communicating with any other Citizens Radio station, but not promiscuously. In most other landmobile radio services, communication is restricted to radio stations owned or under the control of the same licensee. For example, the crew of a Penn-Central train may not communicate by radio with the crew of a Burlington train, except in emergencies. Mr. Brown may talk by Citizens Radio with Mrs. Brown or other persons who operate Citizens Radio stations under his control. He may also talk with Mr. Smith or anyone else who operates a licensed Citizens Radio station, not under Mr. Brown's control, but he should do so only by pre-arrangement, in emergencies, or under other such circumstances.

He can permit an employee or an immediate member of his

family to talk over his radio equipment, but he, as licensee, is held responsible for the proper operation of the equipment. He cannot exact a fee from anyone for the use of his radio equipment.

Only a station license is required. An operator's license is *not* required. A single radio-station license can cover any number of radio transmitters under the control of the same licensee in the same geographical area.

Before Citizens Radio

Until the Citizens Radio Service was established by the Federal Communications Commission, the use of two-way radiotelephony was restricted to local and national governmental agencies, certain kinds of commercial enterprises, and radio amateurs. It was comparable to restricting the use of publicly owned highways to military vehicles, police cars, fire trucks, buses, taxicabs, trucks, and sportscar enthusiasts, banning private autos from using any roads except those within the owner's property.

The radio spectrum is a very wide band of radio frequencies extending from around 10 kilohertz (KH_z), which is 10,000 cycles per second (cps.) to around 35,000 megahertz (MH_z), which is 35 billion cps. A radio channel can be likened to a traffic lane. A radio transmitter that conveys speech only requires a lane varying in width from about 4 KH_z to 30 KH_z depending upon the quality desired and the method used to apply the speech to the radio carrier wave at the transmitter. A standard AM (amplitude modulated) broadcasting station occupies a lane only 10 to 30 KH_z wide while an FM (frequency modulated) broadcasting station occupies a lane or a channel that is 150 to 200 KH_z wide. A TV station uses a lane or channel that is 6,000 KH_z wide in order to accommodate both picture and sound signals.

While it would seem that there is ample room for a private channel or traffic lane for almost everyone who would like to use one, there are actually far fewer radio channels than prospective users. Thus, first consideration had to be given by the government to those whose use of radio channels was in the interest of public safety, necessity, and convenience. Among the first were ships. Obviously, the ability to communicate among ships as well as between ships and shore was in the interests of public safety. Today, about 250,000 ships and pleasure craft are licensed to use two-way radio.

When suitable equipment became available, police departments equipped patrol cars with two-way radio. Again, public safety was served. Electric power utility trucks were permitted to use radio because the work performed by their crews served public necessity. Radio in taxicabs served public convenience.

Several parts of the radio spectrum, comparable to broad highways, were allocated to radio amateurs. While the several hundred thousands of hams do not directly serve public safety, necessity, or convenience, they have performed meritorious service in times of disaster. They also have discovered, pioneered, and developed technological advances which have earned them the right to use valuable radio spectrum space. Also, the hams provide the nation with an immediately available communications network which can be put to use if a national emergency should so require.

But, many businessmen who could use two-way radio profitably were denied the right to do so. Specifically excluded were service businesses such as radio-TV repairmen, plumbers, and even the REA Express Company.

The Citizens Radio Service

However, the radio spectrum belongs to the public and the Federal Communications Commission (FCC) established the Citizens Radio Service in order to permit those previously ineligible for other radio services to have some space in the radio spectrum. It became possible for any citizen over 18 years of age to apply for a free radio-station license which would authorize him or her to set up and then to operate a private two-way radio communications system.

In 1949, the FCC assigned a 10-MH$_z$-wide band between 460 and 470 MH$_z$ to the Citizens Radio Service. This very wide communications highway could be divided into from 200 to 500 separate channels or traffic lanes. While all other radio stations were assigned a specific channel or lane, Citizens Radio stations were initially permitted to operate on any frequency within the limits of the band, without regard to its possible occupancy by many others.

At the start, however, there was no mad rush by the public to use this superhighway, mainly because there was no suitable equipment available at reasonable cost. When equipment did become available in large quantities, it cost upwards of $700 to equip a vehicle with a Citizens radiotelephone.

Over a period of a few years, businessmen who were ineligible for radio-station licenses on specifically assigned channels in the other radio services did install Citizens radiotelephones which often cost more than the radios used in police cars or taxicabs. Since specific channels were not assigned, chaos resulted in some large metropolitan areas where many tried to use Citizens Radio on an unassigned frequency basis. It was like letting loose several hundred drivers on a wide expressway which is not divided into lanes and where every driver can drive as he pleases.

Poor Man's Radiotelephone

There was one exception. One frequency, 465 MH$_z$, was assigned to all licensees who wanted to use a "poor man's radiotelephone." This one frequency "party-line" had to suffice for all users of low-power Citizens radiotelephones.

The poor man's radiotelephone, it was hoped, would be used by the general public—the butcher, the baker, the candlestick maker, and the housewife. Several manufacturers undertook the development of such a radiotelephone. Only one succeeded; the others, some of whose products actually reached the market, gave up because of difficult technical design and manufacturing problems. Two-way radiotelephones for use on the 465-MH$_z$ party-line channel, which sold for as little as about $70 for a single unit, finally became available. Other models were priced between $100 and $200. However, some users were dissatisfied, while many others were pleased. Dissatisfaction was caused by a lack of understanding by the purchaser about the limitations of low-power radio operating in the ultra-high frequency (u.h.f.) range. Others, who did not expect the same range as is possible with a $700 unit, were delighted.

These low-cost radiotelephones operate in the portion of the radio spectrum where communicating range is limited to direct line-of-sight. Under some conditions, communicating range is only a few hundred feet—ample for such uses as communicating from a farmhouse to a barn, for taking inventory in stores and warehouses, and for dispatching materials-handling trucks within a plant area. When installed by an expert or by a neophyte who follows the directions in the instruction book, these units work well. Communication over distances as great as 50 miles between a tugboat at sea and an office in a Manhattan skyscraper has been reported, but this cannot be reliably depended on for day-to-day use.

However, this kind of radiotelephone did not meet the requirements of the professional photographer who wanted to be reached while on the road several miles from home. Nor did it meet the requirements of millions of other people who wanted to have radiotelephones in their cars to keep in touch with home or office. They sought something that would give them the same kind of communications as the taxicab firms and police departments were enjoying.

They could get this kind of communication if they were willing and able to spend upwards of $500 for a radiotelephone per car and not less than $600, and often much more, for the base station equipment. Or, they could subscribe to mobile telephone service, where it was available, at a cost of $30 per month or more for service charges and equipment rental.

Citizens Radio Service Rules Revised

In late 1958, the FCC revised its rules and regulations governing the Citizens Radio Service. A new band of frequencies in the space formerly known as the 11-meter amateur band (from 29.96 to 27.23MH$_z$) was allocated to this service. It was divided into twenty-two individual radiotelephone channels, with a twenty-third channel (on 27.255 MH$_z$) added subsequently. The former 460 to 470 MH$_z$ Citizens Band was reallocated to various services, but forty-nine specific frequencies (channels) in this band were retained for Citizens Radio stations, putting an end to the rampant use that existed when any and all Citizens licensees could operate suitable equipment on any frequency in the band that they chose.

There are now three classes of Citizens Radio stations: class A stations, to which 16 channels are available in the 460 to 470 MH$_z$ band; class C stations, which are used for radio control purposes (no voice transmission) for opening of garage doors, control of model aircraft and boats, and which can use any of six frequencies in the 27-MH$_z$ band and additional channels in the 72-76 MH$_z$ band; and class D stations, to which twenty-three radiotelephone channels are available in the 27-MH$_z$ band. (See Figs. 1-1 and 1-2.)

Class A and D stations are primarily intended for voice communication between vehicles, from a fixed point to vehicles and between two or more fixed points. Class C stations are permitted only to transmit coded or uncoded impulses for remote control of apparatus. Class A stations may employ AM or FM, and transmitter power up to 44 watts (mean output power) may be used. There are no restrictions on antenna height except in regard to potential hazard to aircraft. Class D stations may employ AM or SSB, and transmitter power (mean output power) is limited to 4 watts. The antenna height is limited. It must not extend more than 20 feet above the surface or structure on which its supporting mast or device is mounted, be it the ground, roof of a building, or a mountain top. The antenna can be mounted on an existing antenna tower of any height but must not protrude above it.

Communicating Range

The communicating range of a Citizens Radio system depends upon the surrounding terrain, the power of the transmitter, the type of antenna system used, the effective elevation of the antenna above surrounding terrain, the frequency band (460 to 470 MH$_z$ or 27 MH$_z$) in which it is operated, the sensitivity of the receiver, and the electrical noise (static) conditions in the vicinity of either or both stations communicating with each other.

Communication distance between two Citizens Radio-equipped cars is limited to 2 or 10 miles at best, generally even less, except when one or both cars are on high ground and there are no hills or large buildings between them. The range attainable between a radio-equipped car and a radio station at a fixed point can range from less than 1 mile to 25 miles or more depending upon many factors. However, communication between two stations at fixed locations, when each has a directional antenna system and both

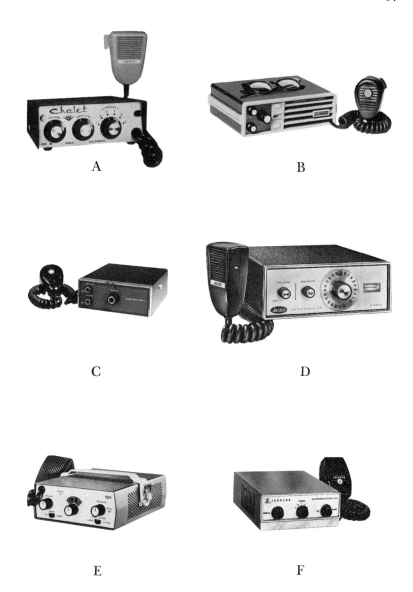

Fig. 1–1. Examples of mobile Class D radiotelephones for use in vehicles, boats, and aircraft. Units shown here are made by (A) Command Electronics, Inc.; (B) Pearce-Simpson, Inc.; (C) Kaar Electronics Corp.; (D) Allied Radio Corp.; (E) Pace Communications Corp.; (F) E. F. Johnson Company.

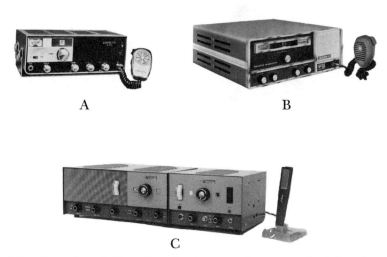

Fig. 1–2. Examples of Class D radiotelephones for use at fixed locations.
Units shown here are available from (A) Lafayette Radio Electronics Corp.;
(B) Pearce-Simpson, Inc.; (C) Browning Laboratories.

are advantageously located, can be considerable (see Fig. 1-3).

Station Licenses

The FCC requires that stations, and this actually means transmitters but not receivers, be licensed. All transmitters must employ crystal control except with special FCC permission. While
various kinds of radio stations are separately defined in licenses
granted in most other landmobile radio services, a class C, or D
Citizens Radio station license only specifies the number of transmitters regardless of whether they are portable, mobile, or used
at fixed locations.

Terms Used

Within the mobile-radio industry, there are various terms used
for designating various kinds of radio stations.

A *radiotelephone* is a radio transmitter and receiver, assembled

Fig. 1–3. With a roof-top antenna at the base station, communication with mobile units within the area of the small circle can be expected in flat terrain. However, a Class D unit equipped with only a plug-in whip antenna used at the top of a hill at Rollings Hills, from where much of Los Angeles can be seen on a clear day, should be able to cover at least the area shown in the large circle, perhaps much farther. It probably will not reach into Hermosa Beach and Redondo Beach because of intervening hills to the west and northwest.

as a single unit or as separate units, which enables two-way voice communication with other radiotelephones.

A *Citizens radiotelephone* is one that meets FCC technical requirements for licensing as a class A, or D Citizens Radio station.

A *mobile unit* is a radio station which is used when in motion or when stationary at any point, but not at a permanent location. A mobile unit may be a radiotelephone carried by or on a person (walkie-talkie, pocket, or belt radio), installed in a conveyance, or one which is moved from one point to another (Fig. 1-4).

A *base station* is a radio station, permanently installed at a fixed location, which is used primarily for communicating with mobile units. It may also be used for communicating with other base stations, but not exclusively.

A *mobile radio system* consists of two or more radio stations of which at least one is a mobile unit. It may consist of mobile units

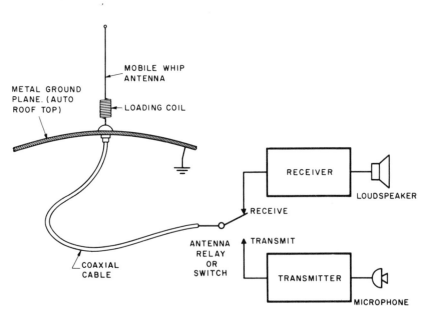

Fig. 1-4. Typical Mobile Radiotelephone. When receiving, the antenna is connected to the receiver. When the press-to-talk switch is operated, a relay automatically connects the antenna to the transmitter.

only or it may include any number of base stations in addition to any number of mobile units.

Mobile-to-mobile communications means intercommunication between mobile units, either directly or via a relay station.

Mobile-to-base communications means intercommunication between base stations and mobile units.

A *fixed station* is a radio station installed permanently at a fixed location for communicating exclusively with other fixed stations.

A *fixed radio system* consists of two or more fixed stations arranged for intercommunication with each other, but it does not include any mobile units.

Point-to-point communications means intercommunication between operational fixed stations or base stations.

A *walkie-talkie* is a hand-held portable radiotelephone. However, *Handie-Talkie* is a registered trade mark applicable to only equipment manufactured by Motorola.

A *packset* is a portable radiotelephone designed to be carried by a handle. Some are operable only from self-contained batteries. Others can also be operated from an external battery when used in a vehicle.

Tone squelch is used in some equipment to keep the loudspeaker silent until radio signals are received which are preceeded or accompanied by a tone or combination of tones at specific audio frequencies. Tone squelch is ordinarily used in Citizens radio systems to lock out unwanted transmissions from stations of other licensees.

Simplex Systems

Ordinarily, Citizens Radio stations operate on a *simplex* basis. In an exchange of communications between two stations, one transmits while the other receives. When station *A,* for example, transmits, station *B* listens. When *A* has completed its message, *B* replies while *A* listens.

A push-button is generally provided on the microphone or the radio unit itself which is actuated when transmitting and released when listening. This is called *press-to-talk* or *push-to-talk* operation.

Most Citizens Radio stations within a system transmit and

receive on the same frequency (channel). Thus, simplex push-to-talk operation must be used since one cannot listen to another station when transmitting on the same frequency (Fig. 1-5).

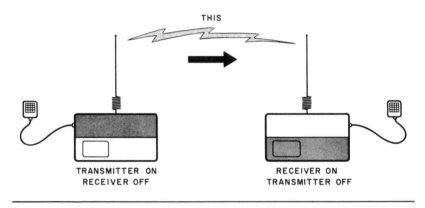

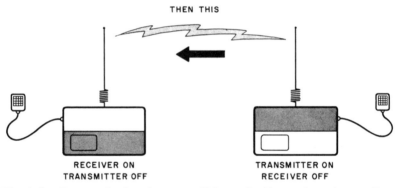

Fig. 1–5. Communication between Citizens Radio stations is usually sequential.

Cross-channel Operation

In a cross-channel system, transmission and reception take place on different channels. Station *A*, for example, transmits on channel 1 and receives on channel 2. Station *B* must receive on channel 1 to intercepts signals from *A* and must transmit on channel 2 to be heard by *A*.

This technique is used in taxicab radio systems to prevent direct taxi-to-taxi communications. All taxis transmit on the base station receiving channel and the base station transmits on another channel to which all taxi receivers are tuned. Thus, taxi drivers hear only the dispatcher, not other drivers (Fig. 1-6).

Duplex Systems

In a *full duplex system,* transmission and reception take place simultaneously. This is the way a standard telephone works. Both parties engaged in a telephone conversation can hear each other at all times and can break in (interrupt) at any time.

Radiotelephones installed on some passenger trains are equipped for full duplex operation so that passengers using the

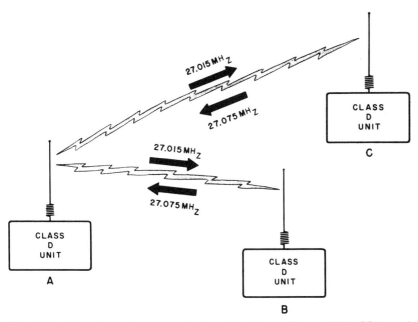

Fig. 1–6. Cross-channel communication. A talks to B on 27.015 MH$_z$ and listens on 27.075 MH$_z$. B does just the reverse. A can communicate with B or C, but B and C cannot communicate with each other. B and C, can hear A, but B cannot hear C and C cannot hear B.

train's public telephone need not be familiar with push-to-talk operation. Instead, they use the radiotelephone in the same manner as their telephone at home.

Mobile telephones provided by telephone companies for use in cars and trucks literally extend land telephone service to vehicles. They operate on a modified duplex basis and push-to-talk operation is used at the mobile telephone. Transmission and reception take place sequentially, not simultaneously as with an ordinary telephone. However, cross-channel operation (transmit and receive on different frequencies) is used to prevent direct intercommunication between subscriber vehicles so that control of communication is retained by the telephone operator. When car-to-car communication is desired, the base station acts as a relay station.

Permissible Communications

Any CB (Citizens Band) operator may communicate with any other CB operator on 7 of the channels listed in Fig. 2-1. The other 16 channels may be used only for intercommunication between units covered by the same station license. Both business and personal matters may be discussed, but no transmissions may be made lawfully unless there is a need to do so. Aimless chit-chat is prohibited.

Manual Calling

Ordinarily, one Citizens Radio station alerts another station by broadcasting the call letters or the name of the person at the desired station. In order for station A to establish communication with station B, for example, the receiver at B must be turned on. It must be set to A's transmitter frequency and someone must be within hearing range of the loudspeaker.

Since Citizens Radio stations are not granted exclusive use of a channel and must share it with other Citizens Radio stations, it is likely, especially in populous areas, that transmissions from unwanted stations will be heard, at least occasionally.

Selective Calling

Means can be provided which will enable station A, for example to push a button or twirl a telephone dial to alert station *B* to answer the Citizens radiotelephone. In fact, the loudspeaker at *B* can be cut off at all times except when turned on manually or in response to a coded signal from station *A*.

Tone squelch can be used in a mobile radio system which mutes the loudspeakers at all stations. When any of the stations in the system transmits, a tone is transmitted in addition to the voice. This tone turns on the loudspeakers of all the stations in the system. The tone squelch is intended to prevent reception from all stations except those within the same system.

When more than one mobile radio system uses the same channel in the same area, any or all of the systems can employ tone squelch to cut off reception from stations of other systems by using a different tone for each system.

Every receiver is equipped with a tone decoder and every transmitter is equipped with a tone sender, which is automatically actuated when the push-to-talk button is operated. The tone decoder responds only to the tone sent out by a transmitter within the same system. Some systems employ a tone which is transmitted continuously when the transmitter is turned on and which is made inaudible by a filter. Others transmit a momentary tone at the start of each transmission.

When it is desirable to signal other stations individually or in groups, without alerting any of the others, *selective calling* is used. Push-buttons are provided which are pressed to call a specific station or group of stations. When a button is pressed, a tone or a combination of tones is transmitted which will actuate a tone decoder only at the desired station (or stations). The tone decoder rings a bell, sounds a buzzer, lights a lamp, or turns on a loudspeaker at the called station.

Or, a telephone dial may be provided. To call station *B,* for example, its assigned code number is dialed. To call *C,* another number is dialed, and so on. The dial causes coded tone pulses to be transmitted. Each station is equipped with a digital decoder which is set to respond only to a specific number.

These refinements, however, cost money. Often, their cost can be justified. Tone squelch is a built-in feature of some class D Citizens Radio equipment and is available as an add-on outboard or inboard accessory. Selective calling, both the push-button and dial types, is available as an integral part of the equipment at additional cost. It can be added to any make and type of radiotelephone.

Cost of Equipment

At the time this is being written, class D Citizens Radio kits combining both transmitter and receiver are available for as little as $40 each. Thus, it is possible to set up a two-station Citizens Radio system with suitable antennas for less than $100. Ready-made class D Citizens Radio transceivers (in which some of the circuits are used for both transmitting and receiving) are available in the $60 to $300 price bracket. When extended range beyond that provided by a plug-in antenna is required, antenna equipment and an antenna support can add from $20 to $100 or more to the cost of each base or fixed station.

The FCC has proposed rules changes (which may be in effect by the time this is in print) that will require all new CB radio equipment to be *type accepted* by the FCC. Manufacturers must submit performance data to the FCC so it can determine if the equipment conforms with FCC technical standards. The new rules would also prohibit the use of external accessories and the replacement of any transmitter parts with other than parts approved by the equipment manufacturer.

How To Get Started

After selecting and ordering the necessary equipment, or after building your own, a station license application should be filed with the Federal Communications Commission, Gettysburg, Pa. License application forms are available from most Citizens Radio equipment dealers and manufacturers or from the local FCC offices (see Appendix). At least 3 weeks should be allowed for license application processing at present because of the heavy workload of the FCC, which in mid-1969 was processing over 20,000 applications a month for class D licenses alone.

The transmitter must *not* be turned on when connected to an antenna unless a valid station license is on hand. There are severe penalties for operation of an unlicensed radio transmitter in violation of FCC rules.

Part 95 of the FCC Rules and Regulations (Citizens Radio

FCC FORM 505
JUNE 1965

UNITED STATES OF AMERICA
FEDERAL COMMUNICATIONS COMMISSION
WASHINGTON, D.C. 20554

FORM APPROVED
BUDGET BUREAU NO. 52—R123.12

APPLICATION FOR CLASS B, C, OR D STATION LICENSE IN THE

CITIZENS RADIO SERVICE

DO NOT WRITE IN THIS BLOCK

1. Application for Class A station license must be filed on FCC FORM 400.

2. Complete on typewriter or print clearly.

3. Be sure application is signed and dated. *Mail* application to Federal Communications Commission, Gettysburg, Pa., 17325.

4. Enclose $8 fee with application. DO NOT SUBMIT CASH. Make check or money order payable to Federal Communications Commission. The fee will not be refunded even if the application is not granted. Also, fee overpayments of $2 or less will not be refunded. (No fee is required for an application filed by a governmental entity.)

		YES	NO
1 NAME OF APPLICANT BUSINESS NAME (IF ANY) OR, IF APPLYING ONLY AS AN INDIVIDUAL, GIVE LAST NAME FIRST NAME (IF AN INDIVIDUAL) / MIDDLE INITIAL	**9** DOES EACH TRANSMITTER TO BE OPERATED APPEAR ON THE COMMISSION'S "RADIO EQUIPMENT LIST, PART C," OR, IF FOR CLASS C OR CLASS D STATIONS, IS IT CRYSTAL-CONTROLLED? (*If no, attach detailed description; see subpart C of Part 95*)		
2 IF AN INDIVIDUAL OPERATING UNDER A TRADE NAME, GIVE INDIVIDUAL NAME; OR IF PARTNERSHIP, LIST NAMES OF PARTNERS (*Do not repeat any name used in item 1*) LAST NAMES / FIRST NAMES / MIDDLE INITIAL	**10** A. WILL APPLICANT OWN ALL THE RADIO EQUIPMENT? (*If no, answer B and C below*) B. NAME OF OWNER C. IS THE APPLICANT A PARTY TO A WRITTEN LEASE OR OTHER AGREEMENT UNDER WHICH THE OWNERSHIP OR CONTROL WILL BE EXERCISED IN THE SAME MANNER AS IF THE EQUIPMENT WERE OWNED BY THE APPLICANT?		
	11 HAS APPLICANT READ AND UNDERSTOOD THE PROVISIONS OF PART 95, SUBPART D, DEALING WITH PERMISSIBLE COMMUNICATIONS FOR WHICH THIS CLASS OF STATION MAY BE USED?		
	12 IF THE STATION IS TO BE USED FOR VOICE COMMUNICATION, DOES APPLICANT CERTIFY THAT IT WILL NOT BE USED EITHER FOR COMMUNICATION OVER A DISTANCE EXCEEDING 150 MILES, OR FOR THE EXCHANGE OF CHIT-CHAT, IDLE CONVERSATION, DISCUSSION OF EQUIPMENT, OR HOBBY-TYPE COMMUNICATIONS?		
3 PERMANENT MAILING ADDRESS NUMBER AND STREET CITY / STATE ZIP CODE / COUNTY	**13** WILL ANY PERSON, OTHER THAN (1) THE APPLICANT, (2) MEMBERS OF HIS IMMEDIATE FAMILY LIVING IN THE SAME HOUSEHOLD, OR (3) HIS EMPLOYEES, OPERATE THE STATION? (*If yes, attach a separate sheet listing the names and relationship of all such persons and give a detailed reason for their operation of your station*)		
	14 IF APPLICANT IS AN INDIVIDUAL OR A PARTNERSHIP, ARE YOU OR ANY OF THE PARTNERS AN ALIEN? (*If the answer is yes, do not file this application because you are not eligible for a license*)		
	15 IS APPLICANT THE REPRESENTATIVE OF ANY ALIEN OR ANY FOREIGN GOVERNMENT? (*If yes, explain fully*)		
4 CLASSIFICATION OF APPLICANT (*See instructions*) ☐ INDIVIDUAL ☐ ASSOCIATION ☐ GOVERNMENTAL ENTITY ☐ INDIVIDUAL/DBA ☐ CORPORATION ☐ OTHER (*Specify*): ☐ BUSINESS PARTNERSHIP	**16** WITHIN 10 YEARS PREVIOUS TO THE DATE OF THIS APPLICATION, HAS THE APPLICANT OR ANY PARTY TO THIS APPLICATION BEEN CONVICTED IN A FEDERAL, STATE, OR LOCAL COURT OF ANY CRIME FOR WHICH THE PENALTY IMPOSED WAS A FINE OF $500 OR MORE, OR AN IMPRISONMENT OF 6 MONTHS OR MORE? **IF YES, SEE INSTRUCTIONS.**		
5 CLASS OF STATION (*Check only one*) (*See instructions*) ☐ CLASS B ☐ CLASS C ☐ CLASS D	**17** IF APPLICANT IS AN INDIVIDUAL OR A PARTNERSHIP, ARE YOU OR ANY PARTNER LESS THAN 18 YEARS OF AGE (LESS THAN 12 YEARS OF AGE IF FOR CLASS C STATION LICENSE)? (*If the answer is yes, do not file this application. Persons under 18 are not eligible for a Class B or Class D license and persons under 12 are not eligible for a Class C license*)		
6 IS THIS APPLICATION TO MODIFY OR RENEW AN EXISTING STATION LICENSE? ☐ YES (*Give call sign*): ☐ NO IF YES, EXPLAIN UNDER REMARKS	**18** IF ITEM 3 SHOWS A P.O. BOX OR RFD NUMBER, GIVE A DEFINITE LOCATION WHERE THE LICENSEE OR THE STATION MAY BE FOUND. (*DO NOT GIVE POST OFFICE BOX OR RFD NUMBER.*) NUMBER AND STREET		
7 DO YOU NOW HOLD ANY STATION LICENSE, OTHER THAN THAT COVERED BY ITEM 6, OF THE SAME CLASS AS THAT REQUESTED BY THIS APPLICATION? (*See instructions*) ☐ YES ☐ NO IF YES, FURNISH CALL SIGN(S)	CITY / STATE IF LOCATION CANNOT BE SPECIFIED BY STREET, CITY, AND STATE, GIVE OTHER DESCRIPTION OF LOCATION		
8 TOTAL NUMBER OF TRANSMITTERS TO BE AUTHORIZED UNDER REQUESTED STATION LICENSE _____ (*Number*) EXPLANATION MAY BE REQUIRED. SEE INSTRUCTIONS.	*DO NOT WRITE IN THIS BOX* SCREENING ☐ Y ☐ N SIGNATURE ☐ Y ☐ N		

SIGN AND DATE THE APPLICATION ON REVERSE SIDE

Figs. 1–7 and 1–8.   Citizens radio station license application form.

Service), available from the Superintendent of Documents, U.S. Government Printing Office, Washington, D.C. 20402, for $1.25, is required to be read carefully before going on the air to avoid inadvertent violation of these rules.

19. IF APPLICANT IS A NONGOVERNMENTAL CORPORATION, ANSWER THE FOLLOWING ITEMS:	YES	NO
A. IS CORPORATION ORGANIZED UNDER LAWS OF ANY FOREIGN GOVERNMENT? (*If yes, do not file the application because you are not eligible for a station license*)		
B. IS ANY OFFICER OR DIRECTOR OF THE CORPORATION AN ALIEN? (*If yes, do not file the application because you are not eligible for a station license*)		
C. IS MORE THAN ONE-FIFTH OF THE CAPITAL STOCK EITHER OWNED OF RECORD OR MAY IT BE VOTED BY ALIENS OR THEIR REPRESENTATIVES, OR BY A FOREIGN GOVERNMENT OR REPRESENTATIVE THEREOF, OR BY ANY CORPORATION ORGANIZED UNDER THE LAWS OF A FOREIGN COUNTRY? (*If yes, do not file the application because you are not eligible for a station license*)		
D. IS APPLICANT DIRECTLY OR INDIRECTLY CONTROLLED BY ANY OTHER CORPORATION? (*If yes, answer items E through K below*)		
E. GIVE NAME AND ADDRESS OF CONTROLLING CORPORATION		
F. UNDER THE LAWS OF WHAT STATE OR COUNTRY IS THE CONTROLLING CORPORATION ORGANIZED?		
G. IS MORE THAN ONE-FOURTH OF THE CAPITAL STOCK OF CONTROLLING CORPORATION EITHER OWNED OF RECORD OR MAY IT BE VOTED BY ALIENS OR THEIR REPRESENTATIVES, OR BY A FOREIGN GOVERNMENT OR REPRESENTATIVE THEREOF, OR BY ANY CORPORATION ORGANIZED UNDER THE LAWS OF A FOREIGN COUNTRY? (*If yes, give details*)		
H. IS ANY OFFICER OR MORE THAN ONE-FOURTH OF THE DIRECTORS OF THE CONTROLLING CORPORATION AN ALIEN? (*If yes, answer items I and J below*)		
I. TOTAL NUMBER OF DIRECTORS IN CONTROLLING CORPORATION		
J. LIST ALL OFFICERS AND DIRECTORS WHO ARE ALIENS IN CONTROLLING CORPORATION AND GIVE BRIEF BIOGRAPHICAL STATEMENT FOR EACH ALIEN		

NAME	NATIONALITY	OFFICE HELD

| K. IS THE CONTROLLING CORPORATION IN TURN CONTROLLED BY OTHER COMPANIES? (*If yes, attach information for each of these controlling companies covering the information requested in items E through K*) | ☐ YES ☐ NO |

20. IF APPLICANT IS AN UNINCORPORATED ASSOCIATION, ANSWER THE FOLLOWING ITEMS:	YES	NO
A. IS ANY OFFICER OR DIRECTOR OF THE ASSOCIATION AN ALIEN? (*If yes, do not file the application because you are not eligible for a station license*)		
B. ARE MORE THAN ONE FIFTH OF THE VOTING MEMBERS OF THE ASSOCIATION ALIENS OR REPRESENTATIVES OF ALIENS, FOREIGN GOVERNMENTS OR REPRESENTATIVES THEREOF, OR CORPORATIONS ORGANIZED UNDER THE LAWS OF A FOREIGN COUNTRY? (*If yes, do not file the application because you are not eligible for a station license*)		
C. IS THE ASSOCIATION DIRECTLY OR INDIRECTLY CONTROLLED BY ANY OTHER ORGANIZATION? (*If yes, give detailed explanation*)		

USE THIS SPACE FOR ANY ADDITIONAL INFORMATION OR REMARKS

WILLFUL FALSE STATEMENTS MADE ON THIS FORM ARE PUNISHABLE BY FINE AND IMPRISONMENT. U.S. CODE, TITLE 18, SECTION 1001.

ALL THE STATEMENTS MADE IN THE APPLICATION AND ATTACHED EXHIBITS ARE CONSIDERED MATERIAL REPRESENTATIONS, AND ALL THE EXHIBITS ARE A MATERIAL PART HEREOF AND ARE INCORPORATED HEREIN AS IF SET OUT IN FULL IN THE APPLICATION.

I CERTIFY THAT:

The applicant has (or has ordered from the Government Printing Office) a current copy of Part 95 of the Commission's rules governing the Citizens Radio Service;

The applicant waives any claim to the use of any particular frequency or of the ether as against the regulatory power of the United States because of the previous use of the same, whether by license or otherwise;

The applicant accepts full responsibility for the operation of, and will retain control of any citizens radio station licensed to him pursuant to this application;

The station will be operated in full accordance with the applicable law and the current rules of the Federal Communications Commission;

The said station will not be used for any purpose contrary to Federal, State or local law;

The applicant will have unlimited access to the radio equipment and effective measures will be taken to prevent its use by unauthorized persons; and

The statements in this application are true, complete, and correct to the best of my knowledge and belief and are made in good faith.

| DO NOT OPERATE UNTIL YOU HAVE YOUR OWN LICENSE. USE OF ANY CALL SIGN NOT YOUR OWN IS PROHIBITED. | SIGNATURE: _____ DATE SIGNED: _____ |

(Check appropriate box below):

☐ INDIVIDUAL APPLICANT ☐ MEMBER OF APPLICANT PARTNERSHIP ☐ OFFICER OF APPLICANT CORPORATION ☐ OFFICER WHO IS ALSO A MEMBER OF THE APPLICANT ASSOCIATION ☐ OFFICIAL OF GOVERNMENTAL ENTITY

2 ～～～～～

CLASS D RADIOTELEPHONES

The previous chapter covered some of the general aspects of the Citizens Radio Service. Now, we are ready to go into some details concerning class D operation.

A class D Citizens Radio station may transmit voice only, employing amplitude modulation, on *any* of the twenty-three channels allocated to class D stations. No form of radiotelegraphy (Morse or international Morse code) may be transmitted. However, tone signals may be transmitted for establishing and maintaining voice communication between stations when employing some form of tone squelch or selective calling as described in the previous chapter.

A class D station may be operated at a fixed location, moved from one point to another and, when installed on a manned conveyance of any kind, may be used either when the conveyance is standing or in motion. Thus, a class D station may be portable, mobile, or fixed. However, the FCC classes all class D stations as mobile units, regardless of whether they are used in vehicles or permanently installed at a fixed location. This is because even if the unit is connected to a fixed antenna in a home or office building, it may be removed from that location and operated at any other location, even while in motion, without further FCC authorization.

Communication, except in cases of emergency, is limited to other Citizens Radio stations. While primarily intended for providing communication between two or more Citizens Radio stations owned or controlled by the same licensee, intercommunication between stations of other licensees is not prohibited when there is a need to do so. It is even allowed to transmit addressed messages to a receiver for one-way communication.

29

Class D stations may communicate between fixed points, between vehicles, and between vehicles and fixed points. They may not communicate with unlicensed stations nor may they communicate with stations licensed in other than the Citizens Radio Service except in emergencies involving danger to life and property.

Available Frequencies

Initially, twenty-two channels between 29.96 MH$_z$ and 27.23 MH$_z$ (the original 11-meter band) were allocated to class D stations. Since then, a twenty-third channel, 27.255 MH$_z$ has been added. The initial twenty-two channels, identified as channels 1 through 22 in Fig. 2-1, are reserved for *exclusive* use by class D Citizens Radio stations. Channel 23, 27.255 MH$_z$, is shared with numerous other radio services, including railroads, motion-picture studios and on-location crews, manufacturers, businessmen, and taxicabs.

Interspersed among the twenty-three class D channels are six frequencies which can be used by class C Citizens Radio stations for transmitting signals to control model aircraft and open garage doors. Class D channel 23 is among those available to class C stations.

Four of the five channels, 27.235, 27.245, 27.255, 27.265 and 27.275 MH$_z$ which include and straddle class D channel 23 (27.255 MH$_z$), are not available to Citizens Radio stations but are available for point-to-point and mobile communications by various other radio services. These channels have been identified *(A)* through *(E)* on Fig. 2-1.

Since a class D station may operate on *any* of the twenty-three class D channels, a licensee may employ a transmitter that can be normally operated on one channel or a transmitter equipped for transmission on two or more channels (one at a time). The licensee may change the frequency of his transmitter at any time, without first getting FCC permission, provided he is operating on one of the twenty-three assigned channels.

Single-channel Operation

Most of the available class D Citizens Radio equipment is

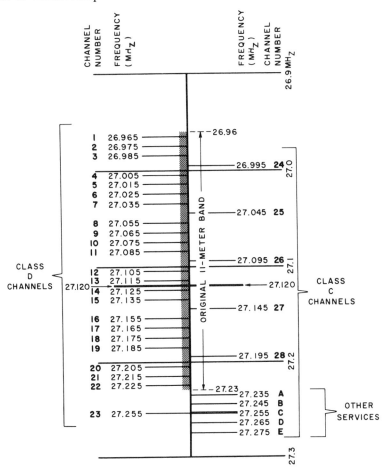

Fig. 2–1. Class D channel chart.

equipped for operation on one channel. Generally, the transmitter and receiver are factory-tuned to transmit and receive on the *same* frequency. Unless specified otherwise by the customer, the equipment manufacturer picks the operating frequency. Some manufacturers, among themselves, have each picked a certain frequency to which each will ordinarily tune his equipment so that the equipment of all or too many manufacturers will not be set for operation on one particular frequency. The customer may change the operating frequency at a later date if he chooses to do so.

Cross-channel Operation

While two intercommunicating stations customarily transmit and receive on the same channel, cross-channel communication can also be used as previously described. One station may be tuned to transmit on channel 1, for example, and to receive on channel 2, while the other station is tuned to transmit on channel 2 and to receive on channel 1.

Multichannel Operation

Nearly all class D radiotelephones on the market are provided with a channel selector enabling the user to switch from one channel to another without having to retune the equipment. However, crystals must be installed for each channel, except for 23-channel units which are factory-equipped with crystals for all 23 channels.

Choosing A Frequency

Some manufacturers have picked channel 9 (27.065 MH_z) as a universal calling frequency to first establish contact, although this channel has not been officially designated as such and may be used for any purpose permitted by FCC rules.

Channel 23 is the least desirable since this frequency (27.255 MH_z) is also available to radio-controlled model plane enthusiasts (class C) and countless other active and potential users of mobile radio in a number of services. This channel is apt to be congested in highly populated areas. In sparsely settled areas, it might not be in use, and, of course, operation on this channel would then be as satisfactory as on any other.

Channels 13 and 14 straddle the industrial, scientific, and medical device frequency, 27.120 MH_z, on which diathermy machines and other creators of radio interference are operated. Near hospitals and clinics, for instance, it would be preferable to operate on other than channels 13 and 14. These devices operating on 27.120 MH_z are only 5 KH_z removed from 127.115 MH_z (channel 13) and 27.125 MH_z (channel 14). Unless a very selective receiver is used, their radiated signals may be heard. Even if the signal is not heard, these signals, if strong enough, can desensitize receivers of class D stations tuned to channels 13 or 14.

Channels 3 and 4 straddle the class C radio-control frequency 26.995 MH$_z$; channels 7 and 8 straddle class C frequency 27.045 MH$_z$; channels 11 and 12 have class C frequency 27.095 MH$_z$ between them; class C frequency 27.145 MH$_z$ is between channels 15 and 16; channels 19 and 20 straddle control frequency 27.195 MH$_z$; and channel 23 is shared with class C radio-control stations which can use transmitters with plate input powers (to the final r.f. amplifier) up to 30 watts under certain conditions. On the other five class C channels, separated from adjacent class D channels by 10 KH$_z$, power is limited to 5 watts. Users of these channels are most likely to operate their transmitters on a sporadic basis, so they should not constitute a serious source of interference.

The FCC rules point out that Citizens Radio licensees are not to expect any protection from interference caused by industrial, scientific, and medical apparatus operated on 27.120 MH$_z$ nor from other Citizens Radio stations with which they share all twenty-three class D channels.

Power Limitations

Class D stations may employ transmitters operated at no more than 5 watts plate power input to the final r.f. amplifier stage of the transmitter. Plate power input is determined by multiplying the plate voltage by the plate current as measured at the final r.f. amplifier stage. For example, if the plate voltage is 250 volts and the current is 20 ma. (.02 amp.), the plate power input is 5 watts. Under these conditions the actual radio-frequency power being applied to the antenna will usually be around 1.5 to 4 watts, depending on circuit efficiency.

Antenna Limitations

The antenna of a class D station may be mounted so that the top of the antenna does not extend more than 20 feet above the surface on which it is erected. The surface, in this case, may be the ground, the roof of a building, or the top of a mountain. When an existing antenna structure is available (broadcast station tower, police or taxi radio-station antenna tower), the antenna may be attached to the tower but must not extend above the tower. The antenna, regardless of where it is installed, may be connected to the transmitter through a coaxial cable (or other kind of transmission line) of any length. Cables of excessive length, however, should not be used as this reduces the r.f. power applied to the antenna.

Equipment Requirements

Transmitters, to be licensable as class D Citizens radio stations, must conform with FCC technical requirements standards. They must be crystal controlled in order to keep them on frequency. Their power-input capabilities are limited to 5 watts. They employ amplitude modulation (AM), or single sideband (SSB) emission, and band-width must be 8 KH$_z$.

The transmitter frequency stability must be better than 0.005 per cent. This means that the crystal must hold the transmitter to within .005 per cent (5/1,000 of 1 per cent) of the frequency of the channel on which it is to operate. On channel 4 (27.005 MH$_z$), for example, the transmitter frequency must not drift above 27.00635 MH$_z$ or below 27.00365 MH$_z$, a tolerance of $\pm1,350$ H$_z$ (1.35 KH$_z$). The carriers of two class D transmitters operating on adjacent channels spaced by 10 KH$_z$ (for example, channels 4 and 5) can thus come to within about 7 KH$_z$ of each other when both have drifted toward each other by the maximum allowable amount. When both are modulated at 3 KH$_z$, their sidebands narrow the gap by an additional 6 KH$_z$ to about 1 KH$_z$, making mutual interference very likely to occur.

The FCC further requires that, if information on the equipment is submitted to them for type acceptance, then the basic operating and adjustment instructions for the transmitter must be furnished to the FCC. A durable nameplate must also be affixed to the transmitter which shows the name of the manufacturer, type or model number, serial number, FCC type acceptance number (when applicable), and the class of station for which use of the transmitter is intended (for example, class D).

If designed for battery operation, the user must be able to replace them without causing the transmitter to operate improperly. Transmitter tuning controls as well as any other controls which by adjustment can cause the transmitter frequency to change must not be accessible from the outside of the transmitter when mounted in its case.

The FCC does not license receivers and has no jurisdiction

over their lawful use except when they cause harmful interference to others (as did some early TV sets) .

Citizens Band Receivers

It is not necessary to possess a class D Citizens Radio in order to intercept transmissions from class D stations. Almost all short-wave receivers, as used by hams, and many of the type used by SWL's (short-wave listeners) can be tuned through the 26.96 to 27.255 MH_z Citizens Band. The Hammarlund HQ-180 AC, for example, (about $495) tunes from 540 KH_z to 30 MH_z This includes coverage of the class D Citizens Band plus many other short-wave services.

To enable reception of Class D stations on boats or in cars, a converter can be connected to a regular AM broadcast band auto or marine radio. Converters of this type are available at radio parts distributors and by mail from manufacturers and mail order houses. Their converter intercepts signals in the 27-MH_z Citizens Band and heterodynes them to a lower frequency (usually 1500 KH_z) within the tuning range of the receiver. Converters are also available for home receivers.

While most class D Citizens radiotelephones combine a transmitter and receiver in a single unit, a separate receiver and transmitter may be used. The transmitter may be a crystal-controlled single- or multichannel device. A suitable AM short-wave receiver or converter ahead of a standard AM broadcast receiver may be used for receiving on any of the twenty-three class D channels.

Increased Talk-back Range

There is a unique advantage in the use of a separate sensitive receiver. The transmitting antenna can only be installed within the previously stated FCC restrictions. However, the receiving antenna can be installed at *any* height. While this will not increase talk-out range, receiving range can be substantially improved.

The base station transmitting antenna might be advantageously located, within FCC limitations, enabling the signal to get through to mobile units. But, the mobile antenna is seldom high off the ground and mobile talk-back range is often less than the base station talk-out range. The talk-back range (reception from mobile units) can be sharply increased by installing the receiver antenna as advantageously as possible. Advantageously usually means high off the ground as well as far removed from sources of interference (ignition noise from passing cars) as feasible.

Home-made Equipment

A home-made Class D transmitter can be licensed under rules existing at the time this is written provided it meets FCC technical standards and is checked out by a licensed technician. However, under proposed rules changes which might be in effect now, only FCC "type accepted" equipment can be licensed for new installations. It is impractical to have a home-made transmitter type accepted.

Commercial Equipment

There are many class D Citizens radiotelephones on the market. They include *transceivers* in which the transmitter and receiver employ some circuits in common; *transverters* in which a converter (to apply received signals to a separate conventional radio receiver) and a transmitter are packaged as a single unit; and *transmitter-receivers* in which completely separate transmitter and receiver circuits are in a single housing. It is also possible to obtain completely separate transmitters and receivers.

Some of the radiotelephones are designed for operation from 6 or 12 volts d.c. or else 117 volts a.c. only, while some have more elaborate power supplies for operation from either a battery or house current. Some are designed for direct operation from dry batteries.

A class D Citizens radiotelephone can be purchased in kit form for as little as $40, while a deluxe, ready-to-use unit may cost as much as $420. All now on the market employ crystal-controlled transmitters. (Noncrystal-controlled transmitters must be approved by the FCC before they can be licensed.) Some employ superregenerative receivers, but most employ a superheterodyne circuit. Generally, the receiver is fixed-tuned to one or more channels (selected for use one at a time), employing crystal control of local-oscillator frequency. In some cases, though, the receiver is tunable over the entire band. Noise limiters are provided in quite a few of the commercially available receivers to reduce the background or interfering noise level. Most are provided with a *squelch,* which in the case of some units is available as an optional accessory. This circuit is useful if the receiver must be left on for long periods of time, since it quiets the receiver completely when no incoming signal is present.

Nearly all new Class D Citizens radiotelephones employ solid state circuitry (transistors) instead of tubes as in the past. Transceivers using transistors are much more compact than tube types and consume much less electrical power. Tube-type equipment, however, is still widely used at fixed locations.

What To Expect

A class D transmitter is a low-power device whose plate input power as defined by FCC regulations is limited to 5 watts. Depending on its efficiency, it may deliver from 1.5 to 4 watts output to the antenna. If it is used with a plug-in whip antenna, it will not talk far under normal conditions. If used with an external longer antenna, range will be determined by the effective elevation of the antenna, the power gain of the antenna (if any), how much power is wasted in the antenna transmission line, the surrounding terrain, and other factors.

One manufacturer guarantees 5-mile car-to-car range under favorable conditions and 10-mile base-to-mobile range, also under favorable conditions. There are circumstances under which the same equipment will not talk 1 mile car-to-car and there are other circumstances where it will talk much more than 5 or 10 miles.

A big city broadcasting station may have a 50,000-watt transmitter. This is power *output,* not input. It is not reasonable to expect the same kind of coverage from a 2-watt output transmitter. However, in the early days of radio broadcasting, a 5-watt broadcasting station, KFBL in Everett, Washington, was frequently heard in Florida.

There are times when class D Citizens Band transmitters will be heard halfway around the world. In the 10-meter ham band, right alongside the 27-MH$_z$ (11-meter) Citizens Band, radio amateurs may talk over distances of thousands of miles with fairly low powers. The radio signals are reliable day and night within a few-mile radius, when the direct wave is depended upon. But, when the radio signal is reflected by the ionosphere above the earth, communication over vast distances is not uncommon. Greatest range is generally during daylight hours and at dusk, with only local communication at night. But, this is not a certainty. Skip transmission of this type sometimes occurs at night too.

This long-distance coverage possibility may not be utilized by the Citizens Band operator since FCC rules prohibit communicating with stations more than 150 miles away. The Citizens Radio Service is intended to provide citizens with short-range communications capabilities. Only radio amateurs may engage in long distance communications.

How To Select Equipment

There is now a large number of radio-equipment houses manufacturing or importing foreign-made class D Citizens Radio equipment. Obviously, there is some inferior equipment, but most of it is excellent. Which to choose depends upon what it is to be used for. Just as the banker knows how to read a balance sheet, the prospective user of Citizens Radio should know how to read a specification sheet.

There is a wide choice of Citizens Radio equipment which may be inspected at radio parts distributors and specialized CB radio equipment stores. They are also described in mail order house catalogs and are sold by large chain stores such as J. C. Penney Company and Sears. Each year, the January issue of *CB Magazine* contains a directory of Citizens Band radio equipment. A copy of the directory issue may be purchased for $1.00 from Publishing Industries, Inc., P.O. Box 60445, Oklahoma City, Oklahoma 73106. Another directory, the *CB Year Book,* is sold at newsstands.

Evaluating Transmitters

Most class D transmitters are listed in their respective specifications as being rated at 5 watts, the legal limit. This is power *input* to the plate of the final r.f. amplifier of the transmitter. It is meaningful only if you also know how efficient the transmitter is. If it is 50 per cent efficient, the transmitter should put out 2.5 watts to its antenna when input is 5 watts. A 30 per cent efficient transmitter will deliver only 1.5 watts.

It is quite possible that a specific transmitter rated to deliver, say, 3 watts, may be able to do so on only one channel or on just a few of the twenty-three available channels. If operation on other than the channel to which a manufacturer customarily tunes his equipment is planned, it would be interesting to know how much power the transmitter will deliver on all twenty-three channels. Remember, however, when power output drops 50 per cent (3db) the received signal is only reduced in strength by about 30 per cent.

In the case of a six-channel transmitter whose operating frequency is changed by operation of a switch that selects the desired crystal, the transmitter might be tuned so that it delivers maximum power output on only one of the channels and somewhat less on the other five. If it is tuned to deliver about the same power on all six channels, usually this represents a compromise adjustment and full attainable power will not be achieved on any channel.

A specification may state that a transmitter is capable of full, or 100 per cent modulation, but it might not state the conditions under which this degree of modulation can be achieved. Power output and talk-out range are increased when modulation approaches 100 per cent. Under these conditions, the voice signals "fill up" the radio-frequency carrier wave. But, overmodulation (more than 100 per cent) must not be permitted. There is bound to be a big difference in the percentage of modulation obtained when a man with a loud voice speaks closely into the microphone compared to that obtained when a woman speaks softly and several inches away from the microphone.

Means for automatically maintaining a high level of modulation is incorporated in some transmitters. A transmitter should be capable of almost 100 per cent modulation with a normal speaking voice. Its speech amplifier and modulator circuits should be designed to attenuate all audio frequencies below about 300 H_z and above about 3,000 H_z for greatest efficiency of operation. This will not result in the highest quality of sound, but the range is quite adequate for voice signals.

Evaluating Receivers

Essentially all Citizens Band receivers now employ a super-heterodyne circuit. Some early models employed a superregenerative circuit which provided excellent sensitivity but poor selectivity. There are two basic types of superheterodyne receivers: single-conversion and dual-conversion. The latter type is usually more sensitive and selective as well as more expensive.

All modern receivers are crystal controlled. This means that channels are selected with a switch (as with a TV set) instead of a tuning dial. A crystal must be installed for each channel to be received except in receivers which employ a frequency synthesizer in which case crystals for all channels are installed at the factory.

Receiver sensitivity is spoken of in terms of so many microvolts (millionths of a volt) input for a given receiver output, generally with a 10-dB signal-to-noise ratio. This means that with a signal generator connected to the receiver input and with an unmodulated signal fed to the receiver, the sensitivity is the number of microvolts of r.f. signal which, when modulated 30 per cent, cause the audio output power of the receiver to increase ten times.

When measurement is being made, only noise is heard (and measured) at the receiver output when an unmodulated signal is applied. When the signal is modulated, the modulating tone is heard mixed in with the noise.

Sensitivity measured in the laboratory is quite different from *useful* sensitivity. When installed in a car, a receiver is in an electrically noisy location. If the noise level input is 5 microvolts, useful signals must be considerably higher in level to be heard. Under such circumstances, the 0.3-microvolt sensitivity of a top-quality receiver cannot be effectively utilized. But, when using such a receiver at an electrically quiet, fixed location, its sensitivity capability will be more effectively utilized.

When the receiver is operable on all twenty-three channels by means of a dial, it will not necessarily have the same sensitivity for all channels, but there should not be a great variation. In the case of a six-channel receiver, it can be tuned for maximum sensitivity on one channel or compromise-adjusted, so it will be almost equally sensitive on all four.

Since the class D channels are spaced only 10 KH_z apart, receiver selectivity is most important when operating in highly populated areas.

Selectivity can be measured by applying a channel-9 signal and then a channel-11 signal to a receiver tuned to channel 10. The selectivity is determined by how strong the signals on channels 9 and 11 must be to produce the same effect on the receiver as a channel-10 signal of normal level.

For example, if a 1-microvolt modulated channel-10 signal produces a 50-milliwatt output at the receiver's loudspeaker terminals, and if it takes a 1-millivolt (1,000 microvolts) signal on channel 9 and on channel 11 to produce the same audio output, the selectivity is 1,000 to 1 (60 db) ± 10 KH$_z$.

Selectivity is important, not only to reject reception of signals on other nearby channels, but also to prevent desensitization by strong (but unheard) signals on an adjacent or nearby channel.

In a fixed-tuned, crystal-controlled receiver, frequency stability is very important. If the local oscillator drifts more than 0.005 per cent it will be less sensitive to on-channel signals and will be more strongly affected by off-channel signals.

What To Buy

What set to buy depends upon your needs and circumstances. If you want riding comfort on long trips and can afford it, you might buy one of the large, heavy, and expensive cars. But, if you need transportation to the supermarket or railroad station, a small, light, and inexpensive runabout will suffice.

When buying a TV set, you can depend upon the reputation of the well-known makers. But, in the decade-old Citizens Radio industry there are some names that are new to the prospective buyer. Some of these companies are not new in electronics, but are new as makers of consumer products.

The criteria should be (1) the specifications, (2) your specific requirements, (3) how the equipment looks to you when you examine it, and (4) the manufacturer's reputation (if you know it). How much you can spend, for what purpose you plan to use Citizens Radio, and the locality in which you live are other factors which should be considered when selecting equipment.

For personal convenience a unit operable on all twenty-three channels provides a great deal of flexibility. But, for business applications a unit operable on one to six channels is usually adequate. A business user generally operates on one channel only. However, when on the road it is convenient to be able to operate on Channel 9 for calling for assistance when required. Channel 9 is the unofficial H.E.L.P. (Highway Emergency Locating Plan) channel.

Table 2-1 lists manufacturers and national distributors of citizens radio equipment from whom descriptive information may be obtained. Following the chart is a list of items (Table 2-2) that should be checked when reviewing a published specification sheet or interviewing an equipment salesman.

Table 2–1   Manufacturers and national distributors
of citizens radio equipment

Allied Radio Corp.
100 No. Western Avenue
Chicago, Ill. 60680
Amelco-Polytronics
1334 West 7th Street
Piscataway Station
Plainfield, N. J. 08854
Autronics Corporation
180 North Vinedo Avenue
Pasadena, Calif. 91107
B & K Division, Dynascan Corp.
1801 W. Belle Plaine Avenue
Chicago, Ill. 60613
Browning Laboratories
1269 Union Avenue
Laconia, N. H. 03246
Channel Master Corp.
Ellenville
New York 12428
Courier Communications Inc.
439 Frelinghuysen Avenue
Newark, New Jersey 07114
Command Electronics, Inc.
R. R. #1
Bristol, Ind. 46507
Echo Communications, Inc.
1038 South Washington Avenue
Cedarburg, Wisc. 53012

General Radiotelephone Co.
3501 W. Burbank Blvd.
Burbank, Calif. 91505
Gonset Division, Aerotron, Inc.
P. O. Box 6527
Raleigh, N. C. 27608
The Hammarlund Mfg. Co.
20 Bridge St.
Red Bank, N. J.
Heath Company
Benton Harbor
Mich. 49022
International Crystal Mfg. Co., Inc.
10 North Lee Avenue
Oklahoma City, OK 73106
E. F. Johnson Company
1226 10th Avenue S. W.
Waseca, Minn. 56093
Kaar Electronics Corp.
2250 Charleston Road
Mountain View, Calif. 94040
Lafayette Radio Electronics Corp.
111 Jericho Turnpike
Syosset, N. Y. 11791
Mark Products Co.
5439 W. Fargo Avenue
Skokie, Ill. 60076

Chas. A. Messenger Corp.
1405 N. Avon Street
Burbank, Calif. 91505
Pace Communications Corp.
24049 S. Frampton Avenue
Harbor City, Calif. 90710
Pearce-Simpson, Inc.
Box 800 Biscayne Annex
Miami, Fla. 33152
J. C. Penney Co.
1301 Avenue of the Americas
New York, N. Y. 10019
Radio Shack Corporation
730 Commonwealth Avenue
Boston, Mass. 02215
Regency Electronics
7900 Pendleton Pike
Indianapolis, Ind. 46226
Sears Roebuck & Co.
3245 W. Arthington
Chicago, Ill. 60607

Sonar Radio Corp.
73 Wortman Avenue
Brooklyn, N. Y. 11207
Squires-Sanders, Inc.
Martinsville Road
Liberty Corner, N. J. 07938
SSBCO
P. O. Box 45101 Northtown
Station
Chicago, Ill. 60645
Tram Electronics, Inc.
P. O. Box 187
Winnisquam, N. H. 03289
Utica Electronics, Inc.
2917 Irving Park Road
Chicago, Ill. 60618
World Radio Lab., Inc.
3415 W. Broadway
Council Bluffs, Iowa 51501

Table 2–2   Equipment specification sheet

Physical

Width ....inches   Weight ....pounds
Height ....inches   Finish ....material and color
Depth ....inches

Electrical

When set to	If a.c. operated:	If battery operated:
"receive":	Line power input....watts	Battery drain ....amps.
"transmit":	Line power input....watts	Battery drain ....amps.
		At what input...(d.c.) volts

Circuit

Total number of tubes ....   Number of transmit channels.....
Total number of transistors ......   Number of receive channels ......

Receiver

sensitivity for 6-db. signal-to-noise ratio . . .. microvolts
Selectivity at $\pm$ KH$_z$ of desired channel . . .. db.
Audio power output . . . . watts
Hum and noise level (below full output) . . .. db.
Audio frequency response $\pm$ .... db. .... H$_z$ to .... H$_z$
Audio distortion at full output . . . . per cent
Frequency stability . . . . per cent

Transmitter

Power input to final . . . . watts
Power output . . . . watts
Modulation capability . . . . per cent
Frequency stability . . . . per cent
Out-of-band spurious radiation . . . . db.
In-band spurious radiation . . . . db.
Antenna output impedance . . . . ohms
Audio frequency response ± . . . . db. . . . . H_z to . . . . H_z

Features

Squelch open sensitivity . . . . microvolts
Squelch drop-out level . . . . microvolts
Audio level loss with noise limiter on . . . . db.

	Yes	No
Tone squelch		
"S" (signal strength) meter		
Modulation indicator		
Universal power supply		

3 ~~~~~~~~

RECEIVER CIRCUITS

Commercial Citizens radiotelephones nearly always employ either a single- or dual-conversion superheterodyne receiver. They differ among manufacturers in sensitivity and selectivity. Some are equipped with noise limiters and/or a squelch circuit. The experimenter can build his own receiver (regenerative, superregenerative, or superheterodyne) for use as an auxiliary receiver or when a separate transmitter is used.

Regenerative Receivers

A very simple receiver that will tune through the class D band, costing only $22.95, is available from Lafayette Radio Electronics Corp. in kit form (the "Explor-Air"). It employs a regenerative detector, audio stage, and rectifier tube (see Fig. 3–1) and operates from 117 volts a.c.

It is also easy to design and build a simple receiver employing any of various circuits. Fig. 3-2 is a schematic of a simple regenerative receiver that can be built. It consists of a regenerative detector, an audio voltage amplifier, and an audio power amplifier. The detector and first audio amplifier may be separate tubes such as the 6J5 or a dual triode such as the 6SN7GT or 12AT7. The audio power amplifier may be a 6V6GT or 6AQ5 and the rectifier may be the old reliable 5Y3GT. Most of the parts are found in the typical experimenter's junk box or are available at most radio parts stores and mail-order houses. Since the various component values are typical, changes in some of the values may give better results with certain tube types.

The coil may be wound on a 1½-inch diameter polystyrene or phenolic coil form. L_1, the antenna coil, may be two turns; L_2 the grid coil five turns, and L_3, the tickler coil three or four turns. All

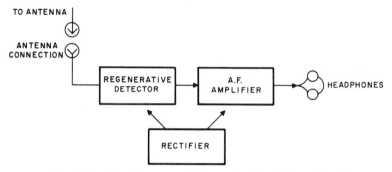

Fig. 3–1.   Simple regenerative receiver for Citizens Band.

three windings may be wound on the same coil form, spaced about ½ inch from each other. The wire may be enamel, cotton or silk insulated, wound so that there is a small air space between each turn. It may be necessary to experiment with fewer or more turns and various inter-turn spacing to get the desired frequency coverage and smooth control of regeneration.

Although a coaxial antenna connector is shown, a binding post will do if a wire-type antenna is used. A regular class D type ground plane antenna, fed through coaxial cable may be used when the coaxial connector is employed.

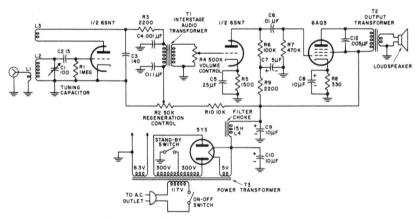

Fig. 3–2   Simple regenerative receiver.

When operated improperly, a receiver like this one is capable of causing unlawful interference to others since, when oscillating, it is actually a transmitter. The regeneration control R_2 must always be set so that the detector will not oscillate. The most sensitive and selective point is just before the point where oscillation starts. It is preferable to add an r.f. amplifier stage between the detector and the antenna to reduce the possibility of radiating an interfering signal.

Superregenerative Receivers

A superregenerative receiver possesses great sensitivity for the simplicity of its circuitry and has inherent noise-silencing characteristics. However, it is not as selective as a superheterodyne receiver and, therefore, it is limited as to its applications. The regenerative receiver shown in Fig. 3-2 can be easily converted into a superregenerative receiver by increasing the value of C_2 and R_1 and connecting R_2 from the grid to the junction of R_3 and C_3. However, the receiver then should *not* be used without an r.f. stage ahead of it since it may radiate a signal which can cause harmful interference. Persons interested in experimenting with superregenerative receivers should consult the various handbooks written for radio amateurs as well as the articles that have appeared in some of the electronics magazines.

Transceivers

The circuitry of the early RCA "Radio-Phone" can be used as the basis for a simple home-made CB receiver. The receiver consists of an r.f. amplifier, and a superregenerative detector, followed by the audio amplifier. Fig. 3-3 is a simplified schematic of the receiver r.f. amplifier and detector. The r.f. signal paths are shown in bold lines, audio paths are shown in dotted lines and d.c. circuits are in light lines.

The signal is developed across the parallel resonant circuit L_2-C_2 and is fed through C_1 to the grid of the r.f. amplifier tube. Minimum bias for this tube is developed across the low-value cathode resistor R_2 and across R_1-C_3 by contact potential. Additional operating bias is developed across R_1-C_3 by the diode action of the grid and cathode in the presence of a signal. The output of

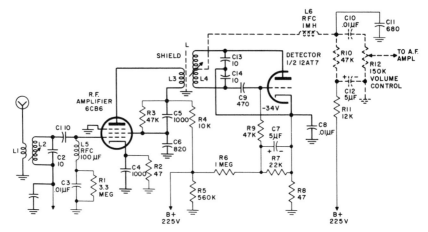

Fig. 3–3.   Receiver portion of RCA "Radio-phone."

the r.f. amplifier is fed through L_3 which inductively couples the signal to L_4. An electrostatic shield is placed between L_3 and L_4 to minimize capacitative coupling.

The detector employs a Colpitts circuit biased so that it will function as a self-quenched superregenerative detector. The audio output of the detector is fed from the tap on L_4 to the audio amplifier through L_6, an r.f. choke coil, which, in combination with C_{11}, removes the remaining r.f. component from the audio signal. The audio signal is developed across R_{10} and the volume control (R_{12}).

Grid bias for the detector is developed across R_9 by the rectifying action of the grid and cathode and charge is stored in C_9. The grid leak is fed to a positive voltage at the junction of the voltage divider consisting of R_6, R_7, and R_8. If the tube could be momentarily stopped from oscillating, and with no signal present, the bias on the tube's grid would be positive instead of negative.

When the tube is functioning, it starts oscillating at the frequency to which it is tuned by L_4-C_{13}-C_{14}. Grid-leak bias is immediately developed across R_9 and C_9. However, *squegging* results, an effect which causes a variation in the oscillator plate current at an ultrasonic rate. Squegging is intentionally achieved by using a high value of grid capacitor (C_9) and a grid leak (R_9) of such value as to complement the capacitor in arriving at this effect.

As the oscillator is squegged, the oscillation is stopped and started at the squegging rate. The same effect is achieved in some superregenerative receivers by using a separate quench oscillator which starts and stops detector oscillation.

By swinging the detector in and out of oscillation at an inaudible rate, the detector is operated at its most sensitive point in a stable manner. There are only two tubes in the entire r.f. section, yet sensitivity comparable to that of some superheterodyne circuits using several tubes, is obtained. This receiver has a rated sensitivity of 1.5 microvolts for 6-db. signal-to-noise ratio. This means that when a 1.5-microvolt amplitude-modulated signal is fed to the receiver input, the audio signal voltage will be twice as great as the noise voltage.

Need For r.f. Amplifier

The superregenerative detector, however, generates an r.f. signal that occupies a wide band because of the squegging action. If allowed to be fed into the antenna, this may cause harmful interference to others. The detector actually is a very low-power transmitter. To prevent radiation of this signal, an r.f. amplifier is used between the detector and the antenna. The amplifier also increases sensitivity and selectivity.

The r.f. amplifier employs a pentode tube. It is often thought that a tetrode or pentode tube does not require neutralization when used as an r.f. amplifier because of the presence of the screen grid. But, it is because of its radiation prevention function that neutralizing of this r.f. amplifier is of importance. If the tube capacity is not neutralized, some of the oscillating detector's signal will get through the r.f. stage into the antenna. When neutralized, the r.f. amplifier is a one-way street, permitting only the passage of incoming signals from the antenna to the detector. But, if not neutralized, the amplifier will pass signals in both directions. The neutralization is accomplished by means of screen bypass capacitor C_6 working in conjunction with the interelectrode capacitancies of the 6CB6 tube. The capacity as well as lead length of C_6, an 820-$\mu\mu$f. capacitor, is critical.

To determine if the r.f. amplifier stage is correctly neutralized, an r.f. detector probe may be used to pick up any leakage signal at the antenna connector. The output of the detector probe is fed through a high-gain preamplifier to an oscilloscope, and the signal may be observed on the screen of the scope. If shortening of the leads of C_6 provides a smaller signal (better neutralization), a smaller value capacitor should be tried.

Converters

A home-made converter can be designed along the same basic lines as a superheterodyne receiver with the omission of the i.f. amplifier, second detector, and audio sections. The local-oscillator components must be chosen so that it can be tuned from 25.365 to 25.655 MH_z to produce a 1,600-KH_z i.f. beat signal (see Fig. 3-4). The output of the mixer is fed to the antenna and ground terminals of an AM broadcast-band receiver, tuned to 1,600-KH_z which serves as the i.f. amplifier, detector, and audio system.

The output of the mixer in the convertor unit may be fed to the associated receiver's input in a variety of ways. Two are shown in Fig. 3-5. Part (*A*) shows C_3, a variable coupling capacitor which is adjusted for maximum output and selectivity. L_1-C_1 are tuned to

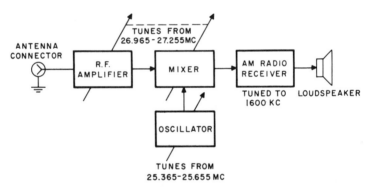

Fig. 3-4. Converter block diagram.

1,600 KH_z. In part (*B*) a cathode-follower stage has been added to the converter for isolation and impedance matching.

Transverters

The Citi-Fone transverter is a transmitter combined with a converter. The Multi-Elmac device includes a conventional class D

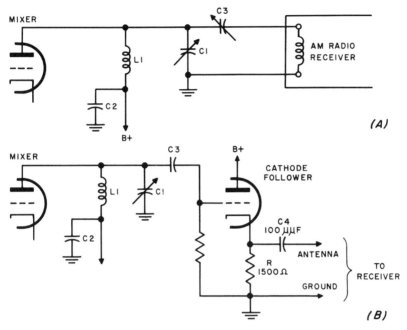

Fig. 3-5. Converter output arrangements.

transmitter consisting of a two-channel crystal oscillator, r.f. power amplifier, and amplitude modulator. The receiver portion, however, is composed of only an r.f. amplifier, mixer and two-channel crystal oscillator. This must be used with a standard AM broadcast radio receiver, which acts as the i.f. amplifier, detector, and audio system. In other words, in addition to the transverter, an ordinary AM radio receiver is required. In a vehicular installation, an auto radio is used with the transverter. Fig. 3-6 shows how an AM radio receiver is used with the transverter to form a dual-conversion superheterodyne receiver.

Transceiver

Nearly all Citizens Band radiotelephones are "transceivers". Some are transmitter-receivers with separate circuits for each. In a transceiver, some of the circuits are used for both transmission and reception. Generally, the receiver a.f. amplifier is used as the modulator when transmitting and the same power supply is used at all times.

For the sake of economy, other circuits are also shared in some transceivers. The antenna matching and tuning circuits for example, can be used as both the receiver input circuit and the transmitter output circuit since transmission and reception take place alternately, not simultaneously.

Nevertheless, the receiver circuitry of a transceiver is functionally the same as that of any other Citizens Band receiver.

Superheterodyne Receivers

A conventional single-conversion superheterodyne receiver consists of a mixer, local oscillator, i.f. amplifier, detector, and audio amplifier [see Fig. 3-7(A)]. It may also have an r.f. amplifier ahead of the mixer, and it may include a noise limiter and a squelch. The r.f. amplifier (when used) and the mixer are tuned to the operating frequency within the 27-MH$_z$ band. The local oscillator is tuned to the operating frequency plus or minus the intermediate frequency. The i.f. amplifier is tuned to either the frequency of the oscillator frequency plus the operating frequency beat signal or the oscillator frequency minus the operating fre-

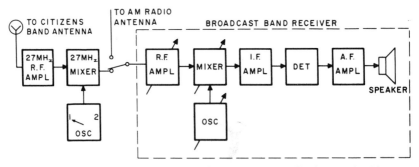

Fig. 3–6.   The transverter converts a home or auto radio into a double conversion superheterodyne.

quency beat signal. If the receiver is tuned to operate at 27.115 MH$_z$ and the i.f. amplifier is tuned to 10 MH$_z$, the local oscillator must be tuned to either 17.115 MH$_z$ or 37.115 MH$_z$.

In a double-conversion superheterodyne receiver, Fig. 3-7(B), there are two mixers and two local oscillators. In a popular class D receiver the first local oscillator is tuned to 19.115 MH$_z$ to provide reception of a 27.115-MH$_z$ signal. Since there is no i.f. amplifier following the first mixer, the resultant 8-MH$_z$ beat signal is fed to the second mixer where it is mixed with a 7.535-MH$_z$ signal from the second local oscillator. The difference frequency of 465 KH$_z$ is fed to an i.f. amplifier tuned to that frequency.

Fig. 3-8 is a complete schematic diagram of a typical Citizens Band receiver. The unit includes a single-conversion superhet-

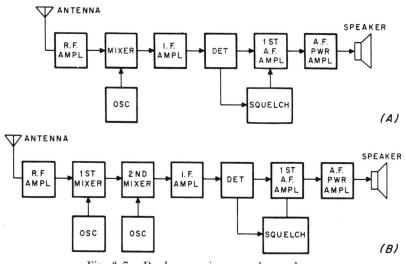

Fig. 3–7.   Dual-conversion superheterodyne.

erodyne with squelch and noise limiter. Crystal-controlled operation on all channels is provided.

This solid state (no tubes) transceiver employs an r.f. stage (*TR-1*) ahead of the mixer (*TR-2*). The signal from the crystal controlled local oscillator (*TR-3*) is fed to the mixer along with the incoming radio signal. The resulting 455-KH$_z$ i.f. signal is amplified by transistors *TR-4* and *TR-5* and then fed to the diode detector (*CR-3*). The recovered audio signals are fed through a noise limiter to volume control *R-30* and then through the contacts of the transmit-receive relay (*RY-1*) to a three-stage a.f. amplifier which also functions as the modulator when transmitting.

The transmitter signal is generated by a crystal controlled oscillator (*TR-11*) whose unmodulated output is fed to *TR-12* which in turn drives the r.f. power amplifier (*TR-13*). Both *TR-12* and *TR-13* are modulated during transmission.

Channels are selected with switches *S-1A* and *S-1B* which are ganged and which connect the appropriate receiving and transmitting crystals for the desired channel. While only two crystals (*R-9* and *T-9*) are shown in the diagram, one for receiving and the other for transmitting) up to seven pairs of crystals can be installed. Another model using essentially the same circuit can be equipped with 46 crystals for 23-channel operation.

Receiver Front Ends

As an example of a typical receiver front end, consider the circuit of the "Citizens Bander Custom" made by International Crystal Mfg. Co., shown in Fig. 3-9. The front end of the receiver section consists of an r.f. amplifier, mixer, and tunable oscillator. By adjustment of the tuning dial which varies the capacity of C_{11}, the oscillator tuning capacitor, the receiver may be tuned through the band 26.9 to 27.3 MH$_z$. While the oscillator may be tuned to beat with any frequency in the band, the r.f. amplifier and mixer are tuned to the one channel most often used (generally the same as the transmitter frequency). The receiver will then be most sensitive at this frequency. Since the r.f. and mixer tuning are fairly broad, reception of other channels in the band is possible without requiring retuning of these circuits.

As shown in the schematic, the incoming signal from the antenna is fed through C_1 to a tap (low-impedance point) on L_1, the r.f. amplifier input coil. The coil is shunted by fixed capacitor C_2 and is tuned to resonance by adjustment of the coil core. Bias for this tube is developed across cathode resistor R_2. In addition, a variable bias from the a.v.c. bus is fed to the grid through R_1. This bias increases as the signal strength increases, decreasing the gain for strong signals and increasing it for weak signals to maintain constant audio output level.

While L_2-C_7 are in the plate circuit of the r.f. amplifier, they actually constitute the input tuned circuit of the mixer, which is a grid-leak biased pentode. The cores of L_1 and L_2 are tuned to the

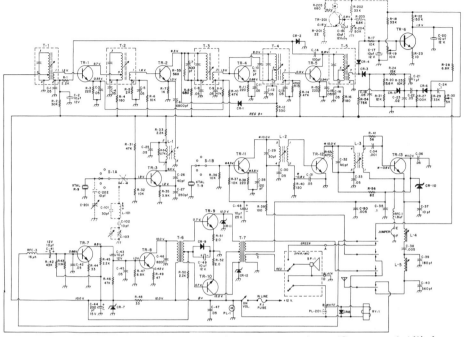

Fig. 3–8. Schematic diagram of solid state transceiver. (Courtesy of Allied Radio Corporation)

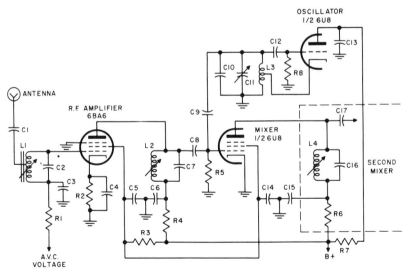

Fig. 3–9. Front end circuitry of tunable receiver.

operating frequency whereas the local oscillator is tuned 8 MH$_z$ below the operating frequency by variable capacitor C_{11}. The oscillator employs a standard Hartley circuit. Its output is injected into the mixer grid through C_9, a low-value capacitor. The plate of the mixer is fed to the input tuned circuit of the second mixer which is tuned to 8 MH$_z$. Nearly all more modern receivers have a fixed-tuned crystal oscillator instead of a tunable oscillator and are therefore intended for reception on only those channels for which crystals have been installed.

i.f. Amplifiers

There is no second mixer-oscillator in a single-conversion superheterodyne receiver and the output of the first mixer is fed directly to the i.f. amplifier. In double-conversion receivers, the i.f. amplifier is fed by the second mixer. The i.f. amplifier is the key to the supremacy of the superheterodyne receiver.

It is in the i.f. amplifier where most of the amplification of the signal takes place and where selectivity can be most easily obtained. In a class D receiver, it is important to reject adjacent channel interference since the channels are spaced only 10 KH$_z$ apart.

In Citizens Radio receiver, i.f. amplifiers employing pentode tubes to get high gain, dual-tuned i.f. transformers are usually used at both the input and output, as shown in Fig. 3-10. Some receivers employ as many as two tubes or three transistors in i.f. amplifier stages to obtain maximum gain and selectivity.

However, there is a limit as to how much amplification can be used because of increasing noise. Excellent selectivity is required. For this reason, some receivers employ a selectivity filter ahead of the i.f. amplifier and then put resistors across the tuned circuits to broaden the frequency bandpass. This also causes some loss in gain. The objective is to get bandpass type selectivity instead of needle-sharp, so that the amplifier will accept the full 6 to 8 KH$_z$ wide (carrier plus sidebands) signal.

Detectors

Most receivers employ a standard diode detector which provides no amplification. In nearly all CB receivers, the same diode that acts as detector also provides the a.v.c. (or a.g.c.) voltage.

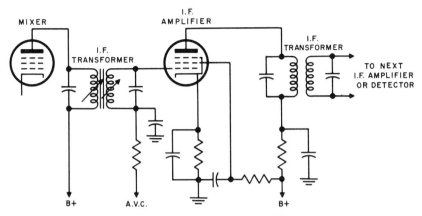

Fig. 3–10. Conventional i.f. amplifier stage.

In some receivers, a separate diode is used for a.v.c. and for detection. Demodulation of an AM signal is no mysterious process.

Either a tube or a semiconductor diode (crystal detector) can be used for demodulating AM signals. This is a point worth considering by equipment manufacturers and experimenters since it reduces standby power requirements by about 1 to 2 watts for tube filament drain alone.

In the output of a diode, whether a tube or a crystal, the demodulated audio signal contains some r.f. This is eliminated by an *RC* network consisting of capacitors which bypass the r.f. and the resistor which, in combination with a capacitor, forms a low-pass filter.

Audio Amplifiers

In receivers which are not equipped with squelch, the audio amplifier is straightforward, generally consisting of two stages, a voltage amplifier and a power amplifier. Often, the receiver audio amplifier does double duty, functioning also as the speech amplifier and modulator when transmitting.

The frequency response requirements of radio communications systems used for transmission of speech are very limited, coverage from 300 to 3,000 H$_z$ being ample. Very little is added to intelligibility by extending frequency response downward, and while an upward extension would add brilliance, transmission of audio frequencies above 3,000 or 4,000 H_z would result in wider radio transmission bandwidth than permitted by the FCC.

The distortion that can be tolerated in a speech communications system can be fairly great without causing irritation to listeners. Since distortion and frequency response characteristics are not at all rigid, smaller output transformers and inexpensive loudspeakers can be used without significant loss of operational quality.

Generally, cone-type permanent magnetic loudspeakers are used, built into the communications unit or transceiver or housed in a small enclosure which forms a baffle or sorts. In noisy locations, more efficient horn-type loudspeakers are substituted for cone speakers because of their better noise-cutting qualities and considerably greater sound output for equivalent electrical input.

Squelch Circuits

The squelch is an electronic control system that silences the receiver when no signal is being received or when a signal being received is so weak that it would be accompanied by background noise. To the user it means that nothing will be heard from the loudspeaker except when a signal is being received. Without squelch, the loudspeaker is always producing an output; the background noise will be heard between reception of radio transmissions.

The squelch, therefore, must be an automatic device which is controlled by (1) the strength of the incoming radio signal, (2) the reduction of background noise when overpowered by a radio signal, or (3) both. In most class D Citizens Radio units, the first type is used, although the second type is also found in some sets.

Signal-operated Squelch

In some tube-type units, a 12AX7 dual triode tube is used in the squelch circuit. One section functions as the audio-frequency voltage amplifier (first a.f.), the second section functions as the squelch tube. Fig. 3-11 shows the d.c. circuits. The bypass capacitors have been omitted from the diagram to make it easier to illustrate the circuit's operation. Also, instead of B+ indications, or the actual power supply, two B batteries are shown. The heavy lines show the audio amplifier section during an *unsquelched* condition when a signal is being received and the audio amplifier is functioning. The tube has normal operating bias (E_1) since its bias is determined only by the voltage drop (E_2) across cathode resistor R_2. There is no voltage drop (E_3) being developed across R_3. The bias voltage E_1 is the voltage between the grid and cathode. In this path are R_2, R_3, and R_4 in series. Since there are no d.c. voltages across R_3 and R_4, the bias is provided only by R_2. The fact that the cathode of the tube is at slightly more than the 52 volts above ground voltage level does not affect operation. Under this condition, an audio signal fed to the grid of the tube will be amplified and will appear as a much larger signal at the plate.

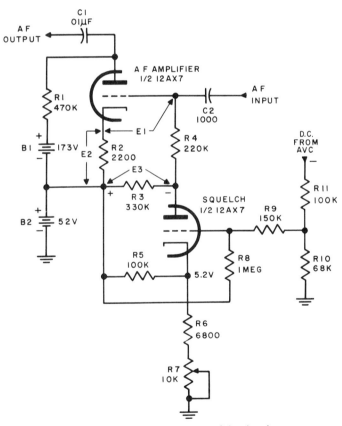

Fig. 3–11. Poly-comm squelch circuit.

When a signal is received, a negative (d.c.) voltage from the a.v.c. circuit biases the squelch tube to cutoff, making it ineffective. The value of this negative voltage depends upon the strength of the received radio signal, this voltage increasing in a negative direction as the signal increases.

But, as soon as the signal ceases or becomes very weak, the a.v.c. voltage drops (becomes less negative). The squelch tube starts to conduct because its bias voltage is now reduced. This tube is biased negatively at its grid by the application of a positive voltage on its cathode from the junction R_5 and R_6-R_7, which forms a voltage divider. The value of this bias is adjusted with the squelch control. R_7. The grid of the tube is also biased by a positive voltage which bucks the negative bias. This positive voltage is obtained from the junction of R_8 and R_9-R_{10} which forms another voltage divider. The negative a.v.c. voltage is fed to the junction of R_9 and R_{10} and subtracts from the positive voltage applied to the grid.

In the squelched condition, the bias on the squelch tube is reduced enough so that it draws current. This current flows through R_3. In the *unsquelched* condition, the voltage at both ends of R_3 is the same, hence the voltage across it is zero. In the *unsquelched* condition, however, current flow through R_3 causes a difference of voltage across R_3. The end connected to R_2 is more positive than the end which connects to the grid of the audio amplifier tube through R_4 and the plate of the squelch tube.

This voltage (E_3) adds to the voltage drop (E_2) in the amplifier cathode circuit. Thus E_1, the bias voltage, is the sum of E_2 and E_3. Since R_3 is 330,000 ohms, even 0.1 ma. flowing through it will cause a 33-volt increase in amplifier bias voltage, more than enough to cut off the tube, rendering the audio amplifier inoperative. This completely quiets the audio stage.

a.v.c. Circuits

The a.v.c. circuit (also called *automatic gain control*, a.g.c.) tries to maintain the sound output of the receiver at a constant level even when the incoming signal varies widely in level. Thus, with a receiver equipped with a.v.c., the signals from weak and strong stations, far and near, are reproduced at about the same volume. If a.v.c. were not used, the signal from a moving mobile unit would vary widely in volume.

In mobile applications, the a.v.c. must also be fast acting to avoid *flutter*. (If the a.v.c. is slow acting, it does not respond fast enough to rapid changes on the level of the incoming signal. The resulting sound caused by these rapid level changes is called flutter.)

a.v.c. circuits operate by rectifying the incoming signal so as to produce a negative voltage whose amplitude is directly proportional to signal strength. This rectification may be done either at the second detector or by a separate rectifier. The negative voltage is then fed back to the preceding i.f., and sometimes also r.f., amplifier to control circuit gain. The greater the signal strength, the more is the gain reduced.

Fig. 3-12 is a schematic of a simple a.v.c. circuit used in many radio receivers. The diode functions as the AM detector as well as the a.v.c. rectifier. The a.v.c. voltage is developed across R_1 and is fed to the grids of one or more i.f. and r.f. amplifier stages through R_2. C_3 is the a.v.c. voltage storage and signal bypass condenser. The audio signal is fed to the audio amplifier through R_3. Capacitors C_1 and C_2 filter out the r.f. component remaining in the demodulated signal.

In some citizens band receivers, a separate diode is used as the a.v.c. rectifier. As shown in Fig. 3-13, the diode tube is used as a shunt, rather than as a series rectifier. The i.f. signal is fed from

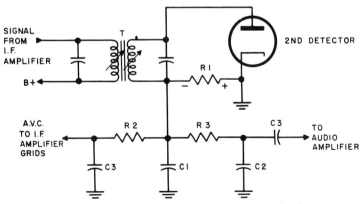

Fig. 3–12. Standard AM Detector—a.v.c. circuit.

the secondary of the last i.f. transformer through C_1 to the plate of the a.v.c. diode which is shunted by R_1. The tube, in effect, shorts out the positive alternations of i.f. voltage but permits the negative peaks to exist. A negative voltage is thus produced across C_2 and is applied to the i.f. grids.

Delayed a.v.c.

Ordinarily, the a.v.c. functions when a signal of *any* strength is received. When there is any signal at all, the a.v.c. produces a negative voltage which reduces the receiver gain. Delayed a.v.c., however, does not function on weak signals, which allows the receiver to maintain maximum sensitivity at times where it is needed most.

With this latter circuit, when the signal rises above a prescribed level, the a.v.c. starts functioning. This is accomplished by biasing the a.v.c. rectifier so that it will not develop a negative d.c. voltage until the signal is big enough to overcome the bias.

The delayed a.v.c. circuit used in some receivers is novel (see Fig. 3-14). The same diode is used as the detector as well as a series a.v.c. rectifier. The audio signal as well as a d.c. voltage are developed across R_1 and R_2. This voltage is also fed to the a.v.c.

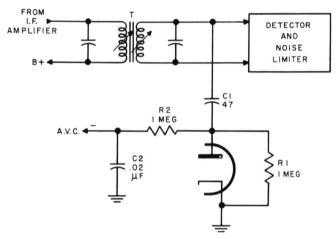

Fig. 3–13.   Shunt-rectifier a.v.c. system.

bus through R_3. A crystal diode which further clips off any re-maining positive component is shunted across the a.v.c. bus. The a.v.c. bus and the diode are biased with a small positive voltage through R_4 to delay the action of the a.v.c. system. The a.v.c. voltage varies from $+0.5$ volt under minimum signal conditions to -5 volts under strong signal conditions.

Noise Limiters

Since ignition interference and other impulse-type noises can be severe in the 27-MH$_z$ band, a noise limiter is often found to be necessary. A superregenerative receiver has inherent noise-limiting characteristics. In an FM receiver, noise impulses are eliminated, or at least drastically reduced, by the clipping action of the limiters as well as the rejection of amplitude variations by the FM detector.

An AM superheterodyne receiver, however, is very susceptible to impulse noise interference. Hams and receiver design engineers have struggled with this problem for many years.

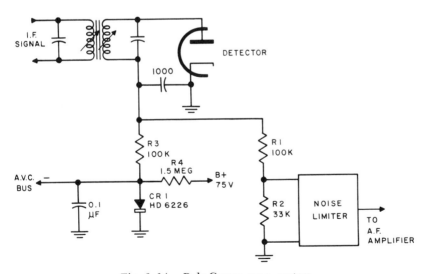

Fig. 3–14. Poly-Comm a.v.c. system.

A simple scheme for clipping noise pulses is used in the Kaar "IMP." It is one of two noise limiting circuits used in this receiver. As shown in Fig. 3-15, a neon bulb is connected between the plate of the second i.f. amplifier tube and B+. Normally, the voltage drop across the i.f. transformer primary and R_1 is insufficient to ionize the lamp. When a strong noise impulse is received, the high voltage pulse fires the neon lamp which acts as a momentary short circuit across the transformer coil. The receiver is disabled momentarily so that neither the noise pulse nor the radio signal get through to the detector.

All *impulse noise limiters* accomplish the same thing. They poke "holes" in the incoming signal. With each noise impulse, the amplifier circuit is disabled. Since the pulses are of very short duration, the "holes" are small and the desired signal is not seriously affected. Obviously, some distortion is caused. For this reason, some receivers are provided with a switch for cutting off the noise limiter when noise interference is not severe. There are also circuits in which the noise silencer is disabled automatically when the received signal is strong enough to override the noise easily.

Fig. 3-16 shows a simple series-type noise limiter. Both the audio signal and the negative a.v.c. voltage appear across R_3-R_4. The noise limiter diode is so connected that its plate will be more positive than its cathode. The plate is at half the a.v.c. voltage while its cathode is connected to a more negative point. While the plate is negative with respect to ground, the cathode is even more negative. Hence, the plate is positive with respect to the cathode. The diode conducts under normal conditions allowing the audio signal to get through R_3, the diode, and to the volume control in the audio amplifier (The diodes may be tubes or semiconductors).

When a noise pulse is received, a large momentary negative voltage appears at the plate of the diode. Its plate is now negative with respect to the cathode since its cathode cannot assume its normally more negative condition until C_2 charges to the new voltage level. Its charging time is extended because of the large time constant of R_1-C_2.

The plate is negative only for the duration of the noise pulse, assuming its normally positive-with-respect-to-cathode condition. During the time the plate is negative with respect to the cathode,

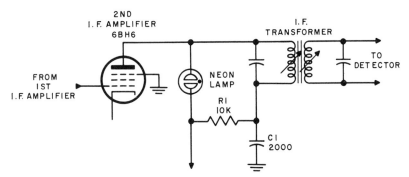

Fig. 3–15. Pulse clipper.

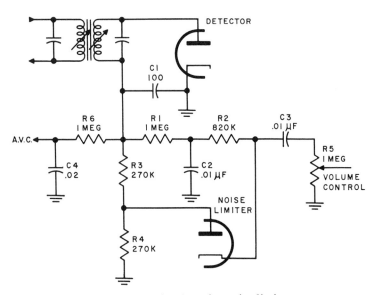

Fig. 3–16. Simple series noise limiter.

the audio signal does not get through. (R_1-C_2-R_2 form a low-pass filter which will not pass pulses.) Thus, the noise pulse does not reach the amplifier. As soon as the pulse has passed, the diode again conducts, allowing audio signals to pass.

Two diodes are sometimes used as limiters. Fig. 3-17 shows the circuit of a full-wave series noise limiter. The cathodes of diodes V_2 and V_3 are more negative than their plates since both cathodes are at full a.v.c. voltage and both plates, while not at ground potential, are at a less negative potential than the cathodes.

As the audio signal swings positive and negative, the d.c. flow through the two diodes is modulated accordingly, and the signal gets through. The noise-silencing action is the same, however, as in a simple series limiter. The plate of V_2 is driven negative, cutting it off and stopping the passage of the pulse into the audio amplifier.

There are various types of shunt noise limiters, one of which is shown schematically in Fig. 3-18. Note that the detector diode cathode is connected to the signal source. Both a.v.c. voltage and the audio signal are developed across R_1-R_2. Capacitor C_3 is charged to the full a.v.c. voltage level, maintaining the plate of the

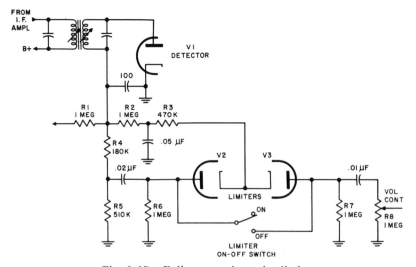

Fig. 3–17.   Full-wave series noise limiter.

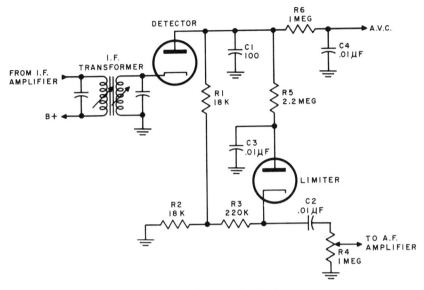

Fig. 3–18. Shunt noise limiter.

limiter diode negative with respect to its cathode. The limiter diode does not conduct ordinarily.

When a noise pulse appears as a momentary negative voltage at the cathode of the limiter diode, the plate is now positive with respect to the cathode. The tube now conducts and, in effect, short circuits the audio signal to ground. The negative noise pulse also travels through R_5 to C_3 to the plate of the limiter diode. However, because of the large time constant of C_3-R_5, the plate cannot readjust itself quickly enough and conducts for the duration of the pulse. After the pulse has passed, C_3 resumes its normal voltage and the diode is again cut off.

Fig. 3-19 shows an automatic disabling series noise limiter. It is a conventional noise limiter except for its automatic disabling feature. The plate of the noise limiter diode is fed to the screen grid of an a.v.c.-controlled i.f. amplifier stage through an *RC* network and a neon lamp. When there is no signal or the incoming signal is weak, a condition when noise silencing is needed, the neon lamp is not ionized. Thus, the d.c. voltage at the i.f. screen does not reach the plate of the noise limiter diode.

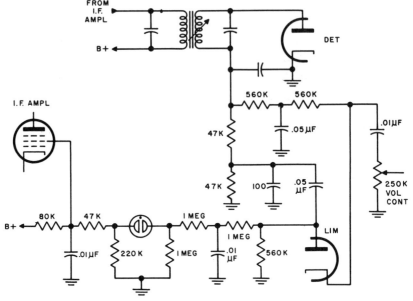

Fig. 3–19. Automatic disabling series noise limiter.

When a strong signal is being received and there is no need for a noise limiter, the a.v.c. circuit biases the i.f. amplifier so that its plate and screen currents are reduced. This increases the screen (as well as plate) voltage so high that the neon bulb fires, allowing the positive d.c. voltage to reach the plate of the noise-limiter diode. This biases the diode so that it conducts freely and stops its noise-limiting action.

This kind of noise-limiter circuit has the advantage that it functions something like a squelch. By choosing the proper resistor values, the noise limiter stops most of the noise from getting through when there is no signal or a weak signal. However, when a strong signal is received, the audio path is made fully operative and much of the distortion caused by noise limiters is avoided.

4 ~~~~~~~

TRANSMITTERS

All class D transmitters must employ AM or SSB, must be limited in plate input power to 5 watts, and must be crystal controlled to within .005 per cent tolerance to be licensable without special FCC approval. Most commercial units employ two or three stages in the r.f. section plus two or three stages in the speech amplifier and modulator section. It is not uncommon to use multisection tubes so that two stages may be included in a single tube envelope.

As one example, Fig. 4-1 is a simplified schematic of the three stages of a simple, single-channel transmitter. The send-receive switching circuits have been omitted for simplicity. The action of the oscillator causes variations in the flow of plate current in tube V_1 since the same cathode is common to both screen grid (functioning as the oscillator plate) and the plate. L_2-C_3 form a parallel resonant circuit, which, when tuned to the oscillator frequency, presents a high impedance load across which the signal is developed. (The parallel resonant circuit also includes C_5 and C_6-C_7 which are in series with C_3.)

L_1, an autotransformer, provides the feedback path for the crystal oscillator circuit, and when tuned to the proper frequency, has an r.f. voltage developed across it. Grid-leak bias developed across R_1 is added to the 2.8 volts developed across R_3, which is in series with the cathode and which acts as a current limiter in case the tube should stop oscillating.

There is provision for two or more crystals in nearly all Citizens Band transmitters. (See Fig. 4-2.) For single-channel operation one crystal is used. For two-channel operation a second crystal is added, and so on. The choice of channel is made by selecting the proper crystal with switch S_{102}.

Each crystal is sometimes shunted by a capacitor with which the

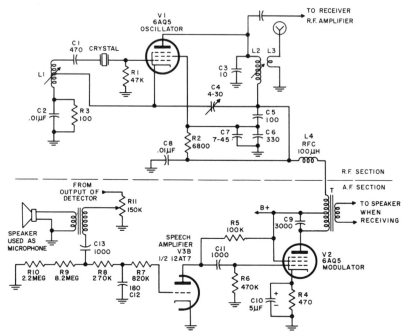

Fig. 4–1.   Single-channel transmitter.

crystal frequency can be varied over a very narrow range to set it at exactly the right frequency. (These adjustments, incidentally, should not be touched except by a suitably licensed operator.) The output of the oscillator, tuned by L_1-C_7, is fed to an r.f. power amplifier stage V_9. The plate tank circuit of the power amplifier is a pi-network.

Capacitor C_{13} is the plate tuning capacitor while C_{14} provides antenna loading adjustment. The indicator lamp (PL_1) glows when the transmitter is functioning and should brighten when the transmitter is modulated. When operated on two channels, tuning is optimized so that the output on both channels will be similar.

In some transmitters, as still another example, crystal frequency is multiplied. The oscillator output frequency is multiplied and then fed to the r.f. power amplifier.

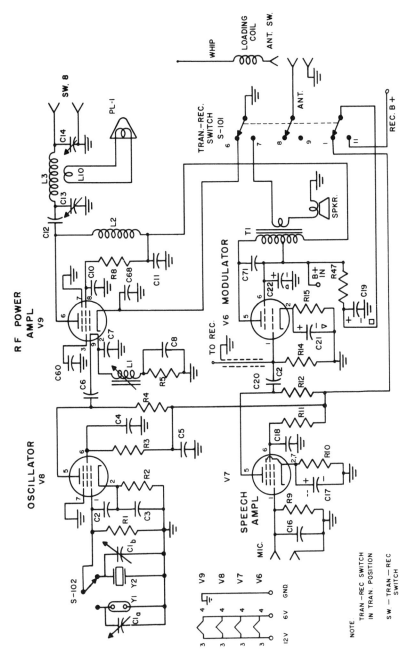

Fig. 4–2. Tube-type transmitter.

Modulators

The percentage of modulation is of importance in getting range. (*Percentage of modulation* equals the difference between the maximum and minimum modulated r.f. voltage compared with twice the average value of the modulated r.f. voltage, multiplied by 100.) The volume of the reproduced voice is partly determined by the percentage of modulation. While the carrier may open the squelch and knock down receiver gain through a.v.c. action, the thing that connects—the level of the sound coming out of the loudspeaker—is determined by the degree of modulation.

When power output of an unmodulated transmitter is, let us say, 2 watts when fed into a 50-ohm antenna transmission line, the voltage across the line is 10 volts, and the current through the line is 0.2 ampere. When the transmitter is modulated fully, or 100 per cent, the antenna current rises 22.5 per cent to 0.245 ampere and the power output increases to 3 watts, an increase of 50 per cent. The power increase is accounted for by the fact that there is power in the radiated sidebands. Of the total radiated power, the carrier represents two thirds, and the sidebands one third, with full modulation.

If the transmitter is capable of 100 per cent modulation, there may be danger of overmodulation which can result in distortion and the radiation of a signal that can cause harmful interference to others. Therefore, the transmitter should be designed to be able to approach but not realize 100 per cent modulation. However, maintenance of a high level of modulation is desirable.

Class D transmitters frequently employ some form of plate modulation. Fig. 4-3 shows the modulator arrangement in the typical class D transmitter. The primary of the receiver output transformer is used as the (Heising) modulation reactor and the receiver audio power amplifier serves as the modulator.

Plate modulation is always applied to the last r.f. stage of a transmitter. That is the stage that feeds the antenna, be it a multiplier, r.f. amplifier, or oscillator.

As shown in Fig. 4-3, the plate of the modulator tube and the plate of the oscillator tube are fed through the primary of an ordinary output transformer (coil L_1) which acts as a modulation reactor. When the microphone is spoken into, the grid of the

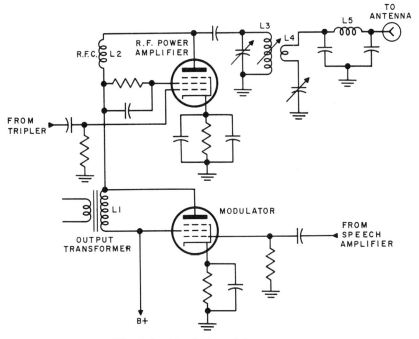

Fig. 4–3. Typical modulator system.

modulator tube is driven alternately negative and positive. This causes the modulator plate current to vary widely, resulting in a widely varying audio-voltage drop across L_1.

This varying audio voltage alternately adds to and subtracts from the B+ voltage applied to the r.f. amplifier plate. As a result the r.f. output increases and decreases in direct accordance with the audio, producing a modulated output wave.

Another technique is the use of the primary of the output transformer as an autotransformer, (see Fig. 4-4). The tapped output transformer winding actually is two windings connected in series, forming a primary and a secondary. This functions as a modulation transformer instead of as a modulation reactor. The audio voltage developed across the lower half of the winding (serving as the primary) is also developed across the secondary which is in series with the d.c. plate supply for the r.f. power amplifier. The a.f. voltage alternately adds to or subtracts from the d.c. plate volt-

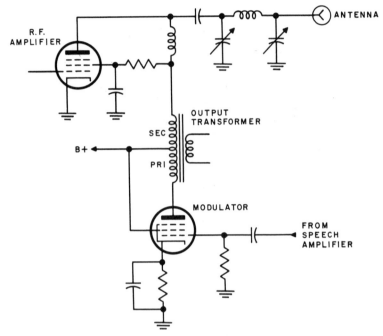

Fig. 4–4. Another modulation circuit.

age, varying the amplitude of the r.f. signal and producing a
modulated output wave.

When a beam tetrode or pentode tube is used as the r.f. power
amplifier, it is customary to modulate the screen as well as the plate
in order to obtain a higher percentage of modulation.

To obtain as high a percentage of modulation as possible
without exceeding 100 per cent, Kaar in its "IMP", uses Heising
modulation with the primary of the output transformer as the
modulation reactor plus an additional gimmick long used by hams
and broadcasters (see Fig. 4-5) . A 1,500-ohm resistor is inserted in
series with the r.f. power amplifier plate supply lead which drops
the r.f. amplifier voltage lower than that present at the plate of the
modulator. This resistor is bypassed for audio (but not d.c.) by a
50-μf capacitor.

Using this scheme, the modulator has a greater effect on the
r.f. amplifier than if both were operated at the same plate voltage.

A reduction in r.f. amplifier plate voltage caused by the modulator will be greater, and an increase in modulator output (passed through C_1) will raise the r.f. amplifier plate voltage higher, resulting in a higher percentage of modulation. While the use of a voltage dropping resistor decreases transmitter carrier output, it presents no problem for low-power class D transmitters. The problem of keeping the power input low enough is more troublesome than getting it high enough.

Incidentally, some sets are provided with test jacks for measuring power input to determine if FCC requirements are being met. As shown in dotted lines, the voltage drop across R_2 is read to measure plate current, and the voltage between the lower voltage end of R_1 and ground is the amplifier plate voltage as interpreted by FCC regulations.

Speech Amplifiers

While separate speech amplifiers and modulators can be employed, many class D transmitters utilize the receiver audio ampli-

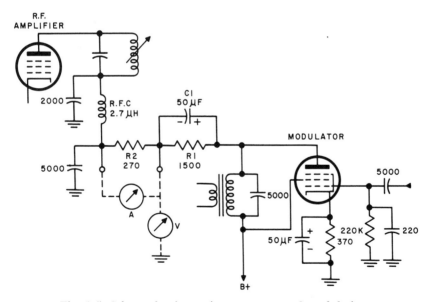

Fig. 4–5. Scheme for increasing percentage of modulation.

fier for this purpose. The audio amplifiers are conventional, usually consisting of a single triode or pentode feeding a beam pentode modulator (doubling as receiver audio power amplifier).

Wide frequency response is not required, and in fact is detrimental. For good speech transmission, passage of frequencies between 300 and 3,000 H_z is ample for good intelligibility. In fact, cutting off the low end response at 500 H_z has very little effect on intelligibility. Therefore, audio amplifier components are selected so that frequencies below about 300 H_z and above 3,000 H_z are attenuated.

Microphones

Ceramic, crystal, carbon, or dynamic microphones can be used. The ceramic microphone is particularly popular at this time because of its moderately high output, its inexpensiveness, and its immunity to temperature and humidity. However, many mobile radio services have stuck with the old reliable carbon microphone because of its very high output and ruggedness. Unlike the others, a carbon microphone requires a d.c. excitation voltage. The other types of microphones are electric generators whose output voltage and frequency vary with the intercepted sound. But, the carbon microphone is a pressure-sensitive variable resistor which varies the amount of d.c. current flowing through it (Fig. 4-6).

The required excitation voltage is derived in various ways. It must be free of ripple and noise which will be amplified if they are present. A dry battery could be used, but since it would require

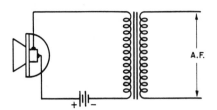

A.F.

Fig. 4–6. A carbon microphone produces an a.f. signal by amplitude modulating direct current.

frequent replacement other means are used. Fig. 4-7 shows how to get the microphone voltage at the cathode of the modulator tube. The modulator bias voltage is developed across R_1, R_2, and R_3 in

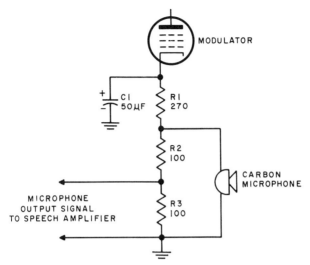

Fig. 4–7.   Microphone excitation voltage can be obtained from modulator bias network.

series with the microphone shunted across R_2-R_3. As the microphone diaphragm is actuated by sound, its resistance varies, causing a change in the current flow through R_2-R_3.

The audio signal developed across R_3 is fed to the input of the speech amplifier. Capicator C_1 bypasses the entire network for audio as far as the tube cathode is concerned.

Another simple microphone technique is employed in the Knight Safari. In this case, a small loudspeaker is used as both transmitter microphone and receiver loudspeaker. This technique is widely used in office intercom systems as well as in large industrial two-way sound systems.

5 〜〜〜〜〜

POWER SUPPLIES

At present, it is still necessary to provide d.c. at 200 to 300 volts for plates and screens of tubes and 6.3 or 12 volts d.c. or a.c. for tube heaters when tubes are used. Solid state mobile transceivers which employ transistors exclusively operate from self-contained dry batteries or mercury cells or directly from a 12-volt vehicle battery.

A class D communications unit may be equipped with a built-in or separate power supply that permits operation from 6 or 12 volts d.c. or from 117 volts a.c.

Fig. 5-1 shows the circuitry of the a.c. power supply used in a typical tube-type transceiver. The rectifier tube provides full-wave rectification of the applied a.c. voltage. The 120-cycle ripple in the d.c. output is filtered out by a pair of electrolytic capacitors.

A power supply for operation from 6 or 12 volts d.c. or 117 volts a.c. also for use in tube-type CB units is shown schematically in Fig. 5-2. A vibrator (VB_1) is used to interrupt and alternately energize first one half of a transformer primary winding and then the other half. This results in square-wave a.c. (derived from the battery) which is made less square by the inductance of the transformer. This a.c. voltage is stepped up and applied to a full-wave rectifier (V_{10}) in the same manner as in the a.c. power supply shown in Fig. 5-1.

The circuitry of the B power supply of still another transceiver is shown in Fig. 5-3. This power supply is operable from 12 volts d.c. (a 6-volt model is available) or 117 volts a.c. When operated from a.c., the vibrator is disabled, and 117 volts a.c. is fed to the second primary winding (P_1) on the power transformer. A part of the 12-volt vibrator primary is used for providing low-voltage a.c. for the tube heaters.

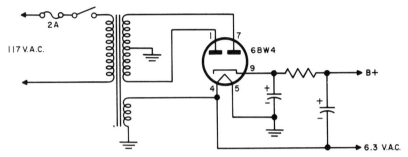

Fig. 5–1. a.c. power supply.

The high-voltage rectifier employs silicon rectifiers in a voltage doubling circuit. The d.c. output is roughly twice the a.c. output voltage of the power transformer.

The change from a.c. to d.c. operation is made by using a different power cord and plug. The circuit changes are made through jumpers in the plug.

Most modern CB transceivers either employ transistors throughout (no tubes) or a pair of switching transistors in lieu of a vibrator in the power supply of a tube-type unit.

Power Source

A class D Citizens radiotelephone consumes very little electrical power, about as much or less than a typical light bulb (commonly 40 to 60 watts). Ordinarily, special arrangements for power are not required. However, a standard power outlet should be available near enough to the radio equipment to avoid the use of long extension cords.

Where line voltage is known to vary widely, the use of a voltage regulator between the electric outlet and the radio power plug will prevent transmitter power and receiver sensitivity from falling off as line voltage drops. A voltage regulator will also extend tube life and keep transmitter power from rising inadvertently to a level beyond the legal limit by preventing the input voltage from rising above its nominal level.

When using class D sets, which employ AM and which are susceptible to more noise interference than classA CB sets, and

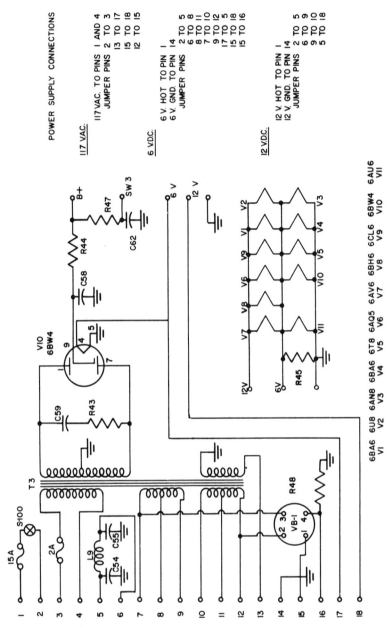

Fig. 5–2. 6/12-volt d.c., 117-volt a.c. power supply.

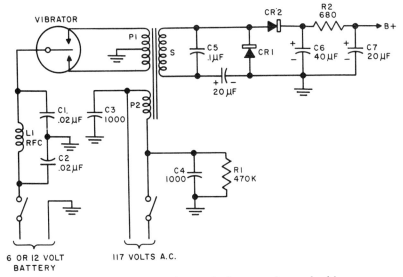

Fig. 5–3. Power supply employing a voltage doubler.

noise interference is objectionable, some of it could be coming in over the power line. A line filter can be plugged into the electric outlet and the radio plug inserted into the filter's outlet. These filters may consist of a single capacitor (about .01 uf.) bridged across the line, a pair of capacitors in series across the line with a binding post at their junction point which is connected to ground, or a more elaborate arrangement utilizing r.f. chokes and capacitors. Sometimes a very simple filter will do the job, sometimes only an elaborate filter is effective. These filters are available commercially or they may be constructed from parts.

d.c. Power Lines

There are still some areas where d.c. power is provided, precluding the use of a.c.-type radio equipment except when using a d.c. to a.c. converter. There are many such converters on the market which will handle the small power requirements of a class D Citizens Radio. The wattage requirements of the particular set in use should be checked in order to determine the rating needed for the converter. They are available in vibrator, transistor, and rotating types.

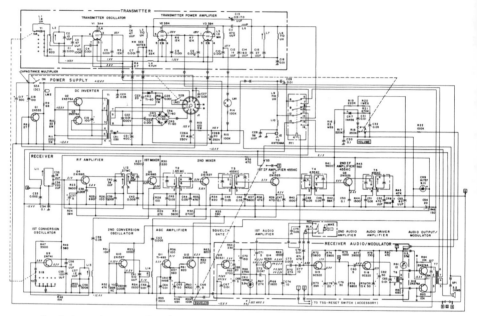

Fig. 5–4. Schematic drawing of a transceiver employing transistors (Q_2 and Q_3) in the power supply in lieu of a vibrator. (Courtesy of The Halli-crafters Company)

A battery-type class D set can be operated from a storage bat-tery at fixed locations where a.c. is not available. In an area where d.c. power is available, the actual power required by the radio equipment can be obtained from the power line. Fig. 5–5 shows an arrangement using ordinary incandescent lamps to drop the volt-age. If the radio unit draws 3.5 amperes when operated from a 12-volt battery, the lamp bank should consist of three 200-watt, 120-volt lamps connected in parallel as shown. In series with the lamps is a 25-ohm, 150-watt wirewound resistor. The radio is connected across the resistor.

The resistance of the three lamps in parallel is 24 ohms (72 ohms each) and is in series with the 25-ohm resistance shunted across the radio unit. The radio unit input resistance is 3.4 ohms ($R = E/I$ or 12 volts/3.5 amps $= 3.4$) . The radio and the 25-ohm resistor in parallel inject about 3 ohms in series with the lamps. The total resistance across the line is 27 ohms. If the d.c. line voltage is 110 volts, the current flow through the circuit is about 4.1 amperes. The voltage drop across radio input is approximately 12 volts. Resistor R dissipates very little power when the radio is connected across it (about 6 watts), but if the radio is removed inadvertently, the resistor will be required to dissipate more than 100 watts.

This system will *not* be satisfactory if the radio unit draws a different amount of current on transmit and receive. In that event, the circuit shown in Fig. 5-6, which requires a 12-volt storage battery, should be used. When the radio equipment is turned off, the power line provides charging current to the battery. When the radio equipment is in use, most of the power is actually provided by the power line. But, if the power line should fail, the battery alone continues to provide power for the radio equipment. The battery also functions as a voltage regulator and capacitor, filtering out noises which may be fed in via the power line. The amount of maximum charging current, which tapers off as the battery approaches full charge, can be varied by using more or fewer lamps in the lamp bank.

Battery Operation

Where no electric power at all is available, a solid state class

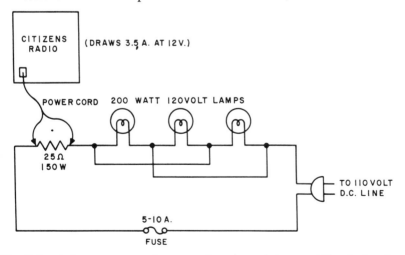

Fig. 5–5.   A battery operated set may be operated from a 110-volt d.c. line through a lamp bank acting as a ballast.

D Citizens Radio unit may be powered from a storage battery.

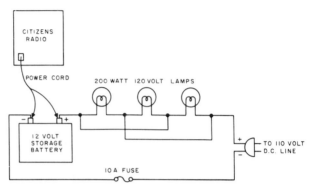

Fig. 5–6. A battery may be used for operation of a Citizens Radio at a fixed location where only d.c. power is available. The battery is charged by the line, the lamps limiting charging current.

As the power is consumed, a freshly charged battery can be brought in. Or, a wind-driven or gasoline-engine-driven generator may be used for keeping the battery charged.

How long a battery will last without a charger of any kind depends upon the current drain of the radio equipment, the ampere-hour capacity of the battery, and the temperature. If the radio equipment draws an average of 0.5 ampere, its consumption rate is 0.5 ampere-hours. A storage battery rated at 70 ampere-hours should keep the radio going for at least 70 hours before the voltage starts dropping appreciably. A 70 ampere-hour battery should provide 0.5 ampere for 140 hours, but the voltage will get pretty low as the battery becomes discharged.

Table 5-1 shows the state of charge of 12-volt and 6-volt lead-acid storage batteries. Voltages are measured under load while specific gravity readings are taken with a hydrometer.

Voltage (12-Volt Battery)	Approx. State of Charge	Voltage (6-Volt Battery)	Specific Gravity Individual Cell
12.60	100%	6.30	1.260 to 1.300
12.42	75%	6.21	1.225 to 1.260
12.18	50%	6.09	1.190 to 1.225
12.00	25%	6.00	1.155 to 1.190
11.70	Discharged	5.85	1.110 to 1.115

Table 5–1 The state of charge in a lead-acid storage battery may be determined by measuring voltage or specific gravity

6 ~~~~~~~~

ANTENNAS

A prospective purchaser of Citizens Radio equipment may ask, "Is there any installation required?" The public has been accustomed to devices which require no installation. The modern movable dishwashers require no special plumbing; table model radios can be used in any room in the house; portable TV sets have built-in single-rod antennas; and there are even air conditioners that can be moved from room to room.

"That depends," the salesman is apt to say in reply, "on what you want to do with Citizens Radio."

To light up the lawn, would you install outdoor lighting fixtures or would you depend upon some light getting through to the yard from the house via the windows? When you operate a Citizens Radio unit indoors using a plug-in antenna, some radio energy will get in and out of the building—but not very much.

If you have one of those pocket-sized portable radio receivers, you can conduct a simple experiment that will demonstrate the value of an outside antenna. If you have an outside antenna for one of your older AM broadcast radios, it will be fine for the test. If not, you can use an ungrounded metal clothesline. Just fasten a wire to one end of the clothesline and make a two-turn coil out of its other end. Connect another wire to ground (water faucet or radiator) and join the free end of the ground wire to the free end of the two-turn coil. Turn on the radio receiver and tune in a weak station. Now put the radio inside the two-turn coil and listen to the tremendous increase in volume. Also, see for yourself how many more stations you can now receive. The antenna system isn't even connected to the radio. The energy picked up by the external antenna is inductively coupled from the two-turn coil to the receiver's internal loop antenna.

85

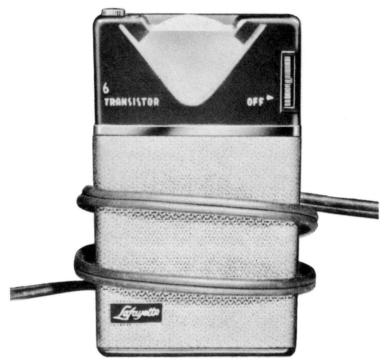

Fig. 6–1.   The range and quality of reception of a small pocket radio are greatly enhanced when its built-in antenna is inductively coupled to an external antenna system. The lamp cord wrapped around the receiver, forming a two-turn coil, is connected at one end to an outside antenna and at the other end to ground. *(Photo by Jacques Saphier.)*

Plug-in Antennas

For short-range communication (less than 1 to 3 miles) a simple, short plug-in antenna will often suffice for the Citizens Radio unit. In a steel-framed apartment, hotel, or office building, it may not, because of the shielding effect of the building. In a frame dwelling, the Citizens Radio will usually work better upstairs than downstairs because of the higher antenna elevation.

The plug-in antenna customarily provided or available as an accessory, may be only a fixed-length or telescoping rod, anywhere from less than 1 yard to as much as 3 yards long.

At 27 MH$_z$, the radio wave is 11 meters in length. A half-wave would therefore be 5.5 meters long; a quarter wave would be 2.75 meters long. Actual half- and quarter-wave antennas are usually cut to about 5 per cent less than these figures. This means that the half-wave antenna would be about 17 feet 4 inches long (208 inches) and the quarter-wave antenna would be about 8 feet 8 inches long (104 inches) or, nominally, 9 feet.

A quarter-wave vertical antenna mounted on the ground or above water forms what is known as a Marconi antenna. The radio equipment may be connected to the bottom of the antenna and to ground as shown in Fig. 6-2. Instead of the earth, a ground plane may be provided for the antenna. This may be a flat, round or square sheet of metal or wire mesh or radials extending outward from the base of the antenna. The radials should be at least as long as the antenna. If a flat sheet of metal or wire mesh is used, the antenna should be mounted at its center and the ground plane should be at least 18 by 18 feet so that the minimum distance from the antenna base to the nearest edge of the ground plane would be about 9 feet, one-quarter wave at 27 MH$_z$.

It is obvious then that when the small radio equipment box itself is used as the ground plane, it has far less surface area than

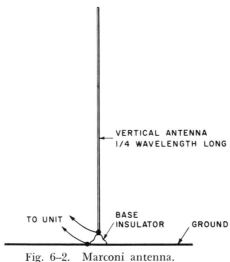

Fig. 6–2. Marconi antenna.

required unless it is directly grounded. While the equipment box and plug-in antenna will work, better performance can usually be obtained if full-sized antenna elements are used.

When a plug-in whip is used, the base of the antenna, which is insulated for r.f. (not necessarily for d.c.) from the equipment box, connects to the antenna circuit of the unit. The antenna is normally connected to the receiver input through an antenna switch or switching relay as shown in Fig. 6-3. When transmitting the antenna is connected through the relay to the transmitter output, which may be a coil coupled to the final r.f. stage plate tank circuit, a tap on the plate tank coil, or a *pi* network output circuit.

Loading Coils

If the whip is less than 9 feet in length, a loading coil is customarily used. The loading coil may be within the unit or it may be a part of the antenna itself. (Fig. 6-4). The loading coil tunes the antenna so that it appears to be longer electrically than it is physically. The shorter antenna then acts as a full quarter-wave antenna. Usually such antennas are not as efficient as full quarter-wave types because of loading-coil losses and a poorer distribution of r.f. energy on the radiating antenna.

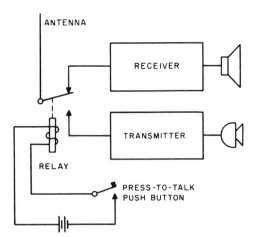

Fig. 6–3. The same antenna is used for transmittting and receiving.

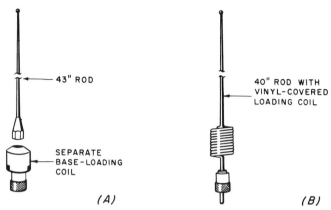

Fig. 6–4. The loading coil may be a separate device attached between the antenna or the radio equipment (*A*), or the loading coil may be a part of the antenna whip (*B*). (*Courtesy: The Antenna Specialists Co.*)

Dipoles

In lieu of a quarter-wave antenna, a half-wave dipole may be used. A center-fed half-wave dipole consists of two quarter-wave elements end-to-end as shown in Fig. 6-5. A dipole may be constructed of two pieces of ½-inch copper tubing or larger diameter aluminum tubing. Stand-off insulators may be used for holding the

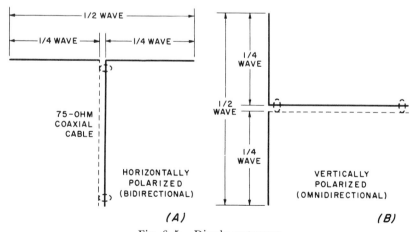

Fig. 6–5. Dipole antennas.

antenna elements away from the mounting surface. A dipole may also be made of 75-ohm TV twin-lead antenna lead-in constructed as shown in Fig. 6-6. Or, regular antenna wire and insulators may be used.

When mounted vertically, the dipole radiates vertically polarized waves. When mounted horizontally, it radiates horizontally polarized waves. Either may be used. With grounded quarter-wave antennas, the polarization is always, vertical. Communication with stations using oppositely polarized waves will be fairly poor. Horizontal polarization is used in TV and is fine for Citizens Band point-to-point communication, but not for mobile communication. This is so since most mobile antennas are vertically polarized.

A dipole is omnidirectional (radiates in a 360° circle) when vertical and bidirectional when horizontal. Thus, when horizontal polarization is used, the transmitter and receiver are most effective in the directions at right angles to the antenna itself.

Feeding the Antenna

The antenna is connected to the radio unit via a transmission line which may be coaxial cable, twin-lead, or open-wire transmission line. Coaxial cable is customarily used. For long runs (100 feet or more) foam-type dielectric coaxial transmission line is sometimes used because it wastes less of the available transmitter power.

A coaxial cable is a concentric line with an inner conductor (wire) in the center of a long tube which is the outer conductor. The center conductor may be a solid or stranded wire insulated from the outer conductor by a solid insulating material called the *dielectric*. The outer conductor is generally a copper braid which covers the dielectric and is, in turn, protected by an outer insulating coat.

When terminated at each end in its characteristic impedance, it is an efficient conveyor of r.f. energy. It wastes some of the power transmitted through it, however, because of electrical leakage and its own resistance. The power loss generally becomes greater as frequency increases. Power loss also rises when the cable is not terminated at both ends in its characteristic impedance, because of standing waves which cause some of the power to be reflected back instead of being absorbed by the antenna.

Type RG-58/U coaxial cable is popularly used with class D Citizens Radio equipment because of its small size and ease of handling. For interconnecting a class D transmitter and its antenna, about two thirds of the available transmitter power reaches the antenna in a 100-foot run of this cable (refer to Table 6-1). Obviously, less power is wasted in a shorter cable.

In addition to the solid-dielectric coaxial cables, there are the hollow coaxial transmission lines in which the inner conductor is centered by insulators at certain intervals or by a spiral of insulating material within hollow solid-wall tubing. These transmission lines are filled with a gas or dry air, sometimes sealed in under pressure, which prevents moisture from entering. Generally, means must be provided for maintaining the desired pressure. Pumps and various kinds of fittings are required for the gas-tight lines.

Type RG-58/U, RG-8/U, and RG-17/U cables have a characteristic impedance of about 50 ohms. These are the most commonly used cables since most Citizens Radio equipment and antennas are designed for interconnection through 50-ohm transmission line. Some antennas, such as a simple dipole, should be fed through 72 to 75-ohm cable (such as RG-11/U or RG-59/U. Only a small loss will be experienced when a 72-ohm antenna, fed through 72 to 75-ohm cable, is connected to a 50-ohm transmitter.

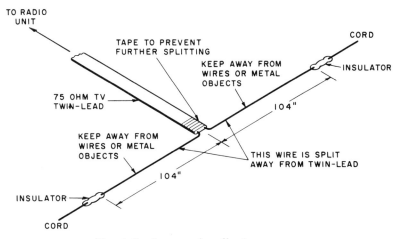

Fig. 6–6. Inexpensive dipole antenna.

Table 6-1   Characteristics of various antenna transmission lines
for 100-foot lengths

Kind of Transmission Line	Class D Loss in DB	Frequency Power Left
Flexible Coax		
RG = 58/U Coaxial Cable (53 ohms)	2	63%
RG = 59/U Coaxial Cable (73 ohms)	2	63%
RG = 8/U Coaxial Cable (52 ohms)	1	80%
RG = 11/U Coaxial Cable (75 ohms)	1	80%
RG = 17/U Coaxial Cable (52 ohms)	.5	90%
Special Lines		
Andrew 83 A Cable (⅜ inch)	.6	87%
Foamflex ½ inch line	.5	99%
Spirafil ½ inch line	.4	92%
Spir-O-Line ⅜ inch line	.6	87%
H 3 Heliax ⅜ inch line	.5	90%
Spir-O-Line ½ inch line	.4	92%
H O Heliax ⅞ inch line	.2	95%
Etyroflex ⅞ inch line	.2	95%
Spir-O-Line ⅞ inch line	.2	95%
H 1 Heliax 1⅝ inch line	.1	97%
Spir-O-Line 1⅝ inch line	.1	97%

Coaxial Connectors

When a special coaxial connector is not provided at the antenna, the cable is connected at the antenna end by soldering the inner conductor to the terminal at the antenna mounting base. The shield (outer conductor) is soldered directly or through a very short jumper wire to the ground terminal at the antenna base.

A plug is used at the other end of the cable, its type depending upon the kind of antenna receptacle provided on the radio unit. A plug that was designed specifically for use with the radio unit's antenna receptacle must be used. Fig. 6-7 shows how various types of connectors are installed on coaxial cables.

Radio frequencies act quite differently from electricity at power and audio frequencies. While connections which would be satisfying for lamps, loudspeakers, and other power and audio frequency devices may appear satisfactory, they may introduce severe losses at radio frequencies. Plugs and connectors used at ends of coaxial cables must be of the appropriate type for the kind of

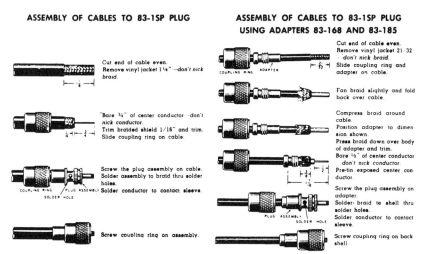

Fig. 6–7.   Assembly of cables to plugs.

cable used and must be installed exactly as specified in the applicable instruction book.

Direction of Transmission

For omnidirectional transmission (in all directions), a vertically polarized ground-plane (Fig. 6-8), coaxial, or dipole antenna may be used. For bidirectional, vertically polarized transmission, a pair of ground-plane or coaxial antennas may be used and oriented so that they produce a figure-8 pattern. For unidirectional transmission (in one direction only) a directional antenna, such as a Yagi, may be used.

Some antennas provide gain. This means that they increase the effective radiated power. Antenna gain is obtained by concentrating the energy—taking some from one place and adding it to energy elsewhere.

Antenna gain is achieved by compressing the radiation pattern. When omnidirectional radiation is required, the energy is diverted so that less is dispersed in an upward direction where it is wasted. The radiated signal pattern, instead of looking like a sphere, takes on a mushroom shape. It is possible to increase the effected radiated

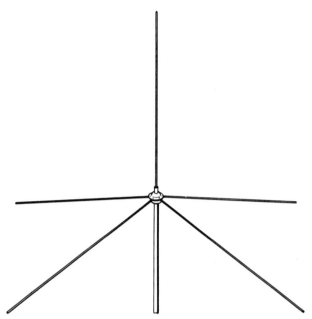

Fig. 6–8.   Full size ground plane antenna for Class D stations has 9-foot whip
and 9-foot ground radials.

power as much as ten times or more through the use of a high-gain
antenna. But a 10-db. (multiplies effective radiated power ten
times) antenna is seldom inexpensive. The ordinary vertically
polarized dipole, ground plane, and coaxial antenna have unity
gain (no gain or loss).

It is easy to increase antenna gain in a specific direction. By
adding a second vertical element to a ground-plane antenna, parallel to and at a critical distance from the vertical antenna radiator,
the second element acts as a reflector. The omnidirectional radiation pattern now becomes heart shaped. This is called a *cardioid
antenna* and radiates a signal twice as powerful in the forward
direction as when a unity gain antenna is used. Its forward gain
is rated at 3 to 3.2 db. which in terms of power gain is 2:1. Hence,
a 5-watt transmitter can be as effective as a 10-watt transmitter.

When two ground-plane, coaxial, or dipole antennas are set
side by side at a critical distance (Fig. 6-9), their waves cancel out in
some directions and add together in the other directions. The
radiation pattern resembles a figure-8. Gain in both directions is

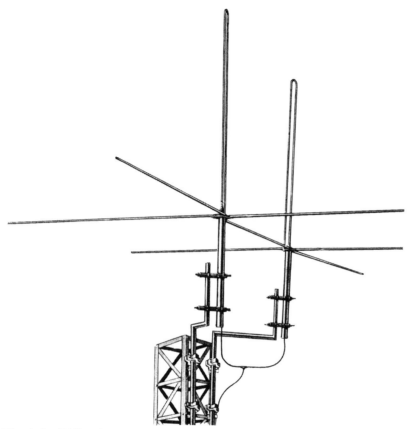

Fig. 6–9. Bidirectional antenna array provides 3.2 db gain in two opposing
directions. (*Courtesy: Andrew Corp.*)

about 3 to 3.6 db., so the effective radiated power in these two
directions. is at least twice what it would be when an omnidirectional unity gain antenna is used.

A Yagi antenna consists of a half-wave dipole, a reflector behind
it, and one or more directors ahead of it (Fig. 6-10). The lengths of
the reflector and directors are critical as is the spacing between the
elements. A Yagi antenna directs the energy straight ahead with
gains of 6 db. or more, depending upon the number of elements.
This antenna can be horizontally or vertically polarized. Two Yagi
antennas can be stacked into special arrays, both transmitting
energy straight ahead, getting the benefit of the gain of both an-

Fig. 6–10. Yagi antenna. (*Courtesy: Scala Radio Co.*)

tennas, or they may point in different directions. The transmitter power is divided among the paralleled or stacked Yagi antennas. Fig. 6-11 illustrates the radiation (or reception) patterns of the various types of antennas discussed.

Examples of Commercial Antennas

There are many types of antennas on the market that are suitable for use by class D base and fixed stations. Some of these were originally designed for use by all landmobile services operating in the 25 to 50 MH$_z$ band. There also are many new types which were designed specifically for use by class D stations and which cost less because more rigid commercial and military service requirements do not have to be met.

The most commonly used type of antenna is the full-sized ground plane using quarter-wave ground radials and either a single quarter-wave vertical radiator or a folded vertical radiator as shown

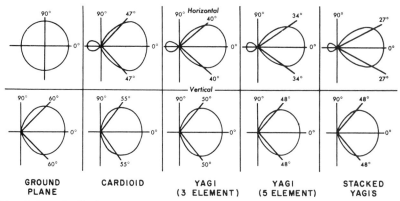

Fig. 6–11.   Radiation patterns of various types of antennas. (*Courtesy: Tele-Beam Industries, Inc.*)

in Fig. 6-12. The Andrew folded Unipole antenna shown is extremely popular in commercial applications. Because of the folded vertical element design, the vertical element is grounded to the

Fig. 6–12.   The Unipole antenna, which is similar to the full-sized ground plane antenna, employs a folded vertical element. (*Courtesy: Andrew Corp.*)

ground plane. It provides a static charge drain path which reduces noise when receiving and also provides improved lightning protection. The folded vertical element is 120 inches in length (when fully extended) and each of the four horizontal ground radials is 114 inches long when extended. The antenna is connected to the antenna transmission line through a plug at the end of the line and a receptacle which is attached to the antenna assembly. The antenna is normally provided with a fitting for RG-8/U (50-ohm) cable. Adaptors are used when employing RG-17/U cable or hollow transmission line.

Antenna Height Restrictions

The height, but not the effective elevation, of the antenna of a class D station is limited by FCC regulations. It may be installed so that its top does not project more than 20 feet above the surface on which its supporting structure is mounted. This means that the antenna may be mounted on top of a pole or pipe set in the ground or on top of a man-made structure of any height. The top of the antenna may be up to 20 feet above the surface of the ground, whether at the bottom of a canyon or on the top of a mountain.

When the antenna is installed on a building, a pipe, pole, or other mast may be used to elevate the antenna. But it must not protrude more than 20 feet above the roof. However, if there is a water tank on the roof that extends above the roof, the antenna mast may be supported by the tank structure but the antenna top must not protrude more than 20 feet above the top of the tank (Fig. 6-13).

Since class D stations are not permitted to use remote control, the transmitter must be within a distance of the antenna determined by the maximum practical length of the antenna transmission line. This is a very definite limitation because of cost and amount of power loss in the cable that can be tolerated. While a 200-foot-long antenna transmission line might be effective, a 1,000-foot line would not only cost a great deal, but the power loss would be excessive.

Installing the Antenna and Cable

The antenna is generally clamped to a pipe or pole with

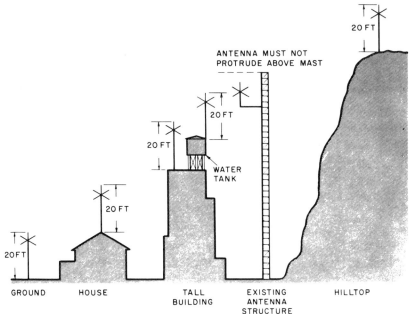

Fig. 6–13.   Antenna height limitations imposed on Class D Citizens Radio stations.

U-bolts. Depending upon the make and type of antenna, the transmission line (coaxial cable or hollow line) is connected directly to the antenna or via a plug and receptacle. Mounting supports should be provided for the cable to relieve strain and to prevent damage to its insulating jacket by striking against other objects.

The antenna ground plane or the mounting at its base which attaches to the pipe or other support can be grounded through a No. 4 or larger copper or aluminum wire to afford lightning protection. The ground wire should take the most direct path to ground and should be connected securely to the ground device. A 6l-foot or longer rod or pipe driven into the ground may be used as ground. The ground wire should have no kinks and should not be wrapped around insulators.

At the radio end of the transmission line a plug should be used which matches the radio's antenna receptacle. The transmission line should be one piece (not spliced). When necessary to make connections as when joining sections of coaxial cable, appropriate coaxial type plugs and connectors must be used. Any other type of connector will cause impedance mismatch, resulting in power losses.

Use of Existing Antenna Towers

A class D Citizens Radio station's antenna may also be installed on an existing antenna structure of any height. But, the top of the antenna must not protrude above the top of the existing antenna structure. If a ground plane antenna is mounted on the side of an existing steel or aluminum antenna tower, it must not be close to the tower since its radiation pattern will be affected.

Since it is generally impractical to install a ground-plane antenna on the side of a tower, some other type of antenna should be used. Cushcraft, for instance, manufactures a center-fed half-wave dipole antenna for this purpose which is provided with a horizontal supporting arm for holding the dipole away from the tower. The dipole may be installed horizontally for horizontal polarization or vertically (parallel to tower) for vertical polarization.

Andrew Corp. also manufactures antennas especially designed for side-of-tower installation. The type 626, for example, consists of two center-fed dipoles spaced one wave length apart. The radiation pattern is influenced by the cross-sectional dimension of the tower and by the manner in which the antenna elements are installed (Fig. 6-14).

Special Antennas

There are various types of class D Citizens radio antennas that solve unique installation problems. These include antennas designed for attachment outside a window or to a chimney (Fig. 6-15).

There are many other types of antennas that can be used, either factory-made or home-constructed. Specific instructions on how to build a directional antenna array for the 27-MH$_z$ band can be found in magazine articles and in the various handbooks for radio amateurs. Most of these, however, are horizontally polarized and are therefore more useful for communication from one fixed point to another.

Single long-wire antennas may also be used. These are directional and provide power gain. Special coupling circuits must fre-

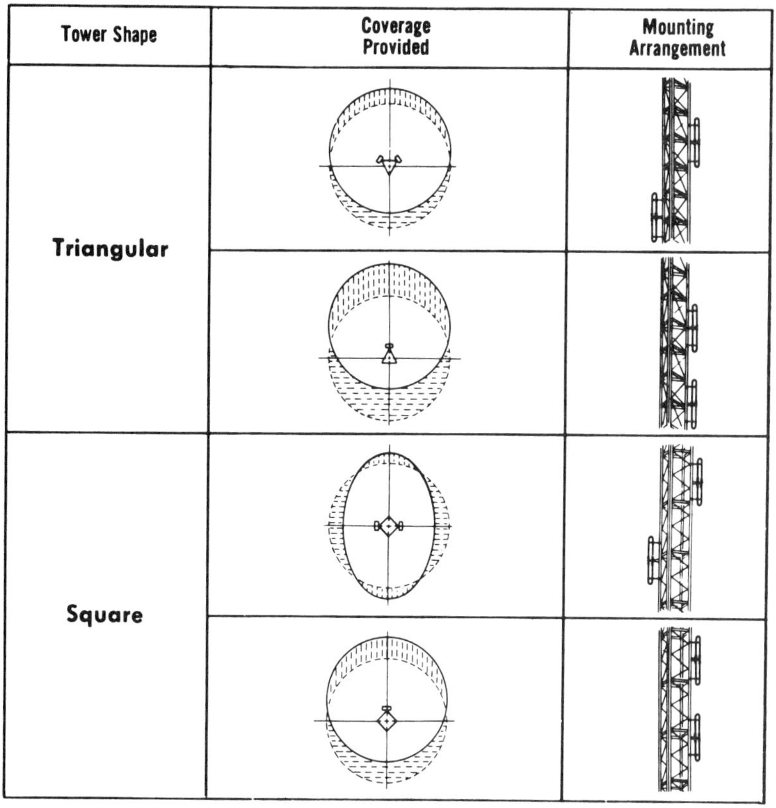

Tower Shape	Coverage Provided	Mounting Arrangement
Triangular		
Square		

Fig. 6–14.   Side-mounted dipoles may be mounted in various ways to obtain different radiation patterns. (*Courtesy: Andrew Corp.*)

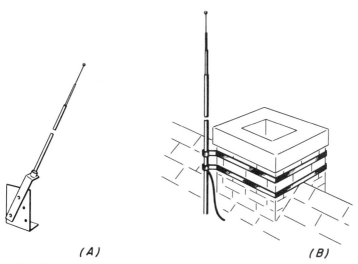

(A)   *(B)*

Fig. 6–15.   (*A*) Window-mounted and (*B*) chimney-mounted vertical whips. (*Courtesy: The Antenna Specialists Co.*)

quently be employed to connect these antennas to the Citizens Band unit.

Antennas for Vehicular Installations

The antenna is an important part of a mobile installation. Since it is not very high above the ground and hence has limited range, it should be installed in a manner that will allow it to function most efficiently.

When installing a class D unit on a boat, a compact one-third-scale ground-plane antenna, with built-in loading coils, can be mounted on a mast as high as possible (even if more than 20 feet above the deck). A full-sized ground plane can be used, but it may be rather clumsy since its radials span the diameter of an 18-foot circle.

A quarter-wave vertical whip (about 9 feet long) may be installed close to the deck or roof of a cabin if a ground plane (such as copper screening) is also provided. Even if a ground plane is not provided, the surface of the water often forms a good ground. Ideally, the radio unit should be grounded to the water by as direct means as possible. This can be done with a short lead to a ground plate, a metal hull, or the boat's engine. Even with the ground lead omitted altogether, there may be enough capacitance between the radio unit and the water to provide adequate r.f. grounding.

Another technique is to use a coaxial antenna, whose elements are all vertical, and attach this antenna to a mast with its base on deck or on the cabin roof. If the boat has a 2 to 3 MH_z ship-to-shore radiotelephone, it may be possible to use its antenna for both the ship-to-shore radio and the Citizens Radio unit, by employing a suitable coupling circuit.

When a Citizens Radio is to be used in an automobile, the antenna should be outside the car. A unit with a short plug-in antenna inside the car will have limited range due to the shielding effect of the car's body (Fig. 6-16).

The ideal location for the antenna is the approximate center of the vehicle's metal roof which can be employed as the ground plane. A vertical antenna, one-quarter wavelength long, would afford maximum performance. The vertical antenna rod, however, would be about 9 feet long. Not only would it look ridiculous on the roof of a car, but it would create a hazard because of the possibility of its not clearing underpasses, tunnels, and low-hanging wires. Therefore it is common to attach the vehicle whip to the rear bumper or to have it protrude from a cowl or fender. It is also good practice to use a spring base to prevent the antenna from being broken off if it hits some obstruction and to minimize vibration effects. See Fig. 6-17 for various kinds of mounting devices.

Because of the objection many have to long whip antennas, several shorter, base-loaded antennas have appeared on the market. When mounted advantageously on a device to minimize radiation

Fig. 6–16. Communication over a short range can be obtained with the Class D unit and its plug-in antenna inside the car, but it will talk much farther if an external antenna is used. (*Photo by Jacques Saphier.*)

pattern distortion by the car body, they may work as well as full quarter-wave bumper-mounted whips (see Fig. 6-18).

Fig. 6–18. Comparison of base-loaded antenna (left) with conventional whip antenna. (*Photo by Jacques Saphier.*)

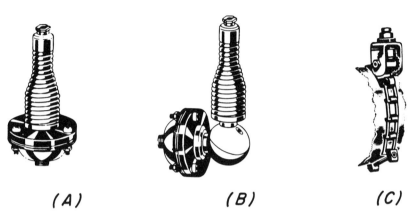

Fig. 6–17. (*A*) Spring base ship antenna mount for vehicle roof or horizontal fender or cowl. (*B*) Universal mounting base permits installation of antenna on a vertical or sloping surface. (*C*) Chain style bumper mount into which the whip may be fastened directly or with a spring between whip and mount. (*Courtesy: Premax Products.*)

7 ~~~~~~~

INSTALLATION

A class D Citizens radiotelephone can be installed in a building, out in the open, or on any type of conveyance. Some types can be carried on or by a person.

To obtain maximum performance, it should be installed in a manner so as to obtain the highest effective antenna elevation in keeping with FCC antenna height limitations. Effective elevation and height do not mean the same thing. The top of a quarter-wave whip mounted on a car's bumper may be only 10 feet off the ground. This is antenna *height*. But, when the vehicle is driven to the top of Twin Peaks in San Francisco, the *effective elevation* will be around 1,000 feet. A base station antenna on top of a pipe on the roof of a 100-foot tall building may have a height of only 20 feet but an effective elevation of 120 feet (see Fig. 7-1).

Battery Power

Power for operation of a radiotelephone in a vehicle or boat is normally obtained from the conveyance's battery unless the unit operates from self-contained batteries. Usually, the battery puts out 6 or 12 volts. While power can be derived from the cigarette lighter receptacle on the instrument panel through a suitable plug, it is preferable to provide a terminal strip which connects directly to the battery.

a.c. Operated Sets

When a Citizens Radio unit designed for a.c. operation only is to be used in a vehicle, a d.c. to a.c. converter is required. This may be mounted on the passenger side of the bulkhead or placed on the floor. Adequate ventilation must be provided. Vibrator, rotary type, and transistor type converters are available. One of the

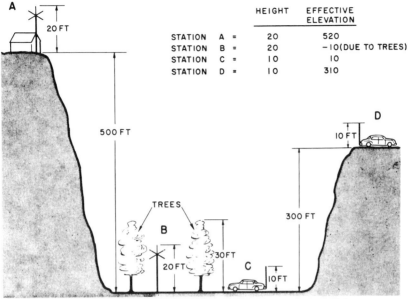

	HEIGHT	EFFECTIVE ELEVATION
STATION A =	20	520
STATION B =	20	−10(DUE TO TREES)
STATION C =	10	10
STATION D =	10	310

Fig. 7–1. Effective antenna elevation vs. antenna height.

newest, the Heath PC-1, available only in kit form, uses transistors. It will handle loads up to 125 watts at 117 volts a.c. and requires a 12-volt battery as its power source. When selecting a converter, be sure it has adequate capacity. It is safer to buy one which is rated at twice the load you plan to apply.

Most of the vibrator types should not be operated without a load. This means that the radio unit's on-off switch should be left on and the radio power plug should be left plugged into the converter, turning the radio on and off by connecting and disconnecting the vibrator converter. Many of these converters are provided with plugs that fit into a cigarette lighter receptacle. For a more permanent installation, the plug can be removed and the input wires may be connected through an on-off switch and a fuse to the battery terminals (see Fig. 7-2).

Direct Battery Operation

A battery-operated radiotelephone is sometimes provided with a wiring kit which includes a fuse holder and battery cables. Some are arranged for obtaining power from the vehicle's ammeter terminals.

Whether the radio unit is to be left in the car permanently or used only occasionally, a terminal block can be installed from which the radio equipment can derive its power. This terminal block may consist of a fuse holder designed to accommodate two cartridge fuses. Since it will have four terminals, two can connect to the battery (or the starter solenoid and car body) and the radio equipment can be connected to the other two terminals through lugs or clips. Since the battery terminals are almost fully obscured by the clamps that lead to the vehicle wiring and body, wires leading to the radio equipment (through fuses) may be attached through solder or pressure-type lugs to the bolts that hold the battery clamps in place. While only one fuse is required to provide protection against short circuits, the dual fuse holder (Fig. 7-3) provides easy and convenient terminations for the wires.

Battery Voltage

In a vehicle, the battery voltage is said to be either 6 or 12

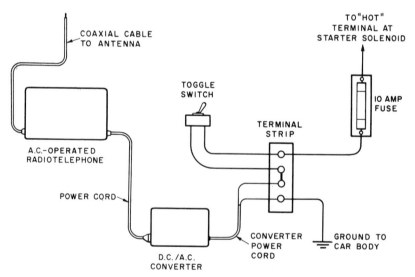

Fig. 7–2. A converter may be permanently installed in a car for operation of an a.c.-type radiotelephone.

volts, but this voltage is only a nominal value. The voltage across a fully charged 6-volt lead-acid storage battery is actually 6.3 volts and 12.6 volts for a 12-volt battery. These voltages are lower when the batteries are not fully charged. With the engine running fast enough for the charging generator to provide battery-charging current, the voltage across a 6-volt battery may rise to as high as 7.5 volts or more and across a 12-volt battery to 15 volts or more. When the voltage gets this high, the headlights are brighter but the lives of the tubes and vibrator (if used in the radiotelephone) are apt to be shortened.

When installing a radiotelephone in a vehicle, it is a good idea to have the vehicle's voltage regulator adjustment checked by a competent mechanic who has adequate test equipment. For a 6-volt battery, the voltage, when measured at the battery terminals, should not rise above 7.2 volts for most cars with the engine running at any speed. For a 12-volt battery, maximum voltage should not exceed 14.4 volts for most cars.

While the voltage across a 12-volt battery may reach 14.4 volts when the voltage regulator is correctly adjusted, the voltage at the tube heaters is not quite that high because there is a voltage drop in the interconnecting wires and connections. Note that a total

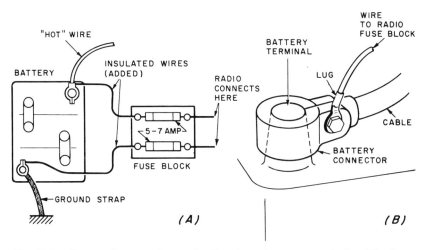

Fig. 7–3. Connections can be made directly to battery terminals. (*B*) shows method of making connection at battery terminal.

wiring and connection resistance of only ½ ohm would cause a voltage drop of 2 volts with a typical current flow of 4 amps. from a 14-volt source.

Oversized Generator

The vehicle's generator should be able to provide ample battery-charging current to take care of the added load imposed by a class D radio unit. However, it may be desirable to install an over-sized generator if the radio equipment is used much of the time. Both d.c. generators and alternator-rectifier generating systems that are specifically designed for this purpose are available. They provide high charging current even at low engine speeds.

Ignition Noise

Unfortunately, vehicular ignition noise seems to be very high at around 27 MH_z. This may seriously limit the usefulness of a class D unit unless some means are taken to minimize its effect.

A suppressor should be installed in the wire connecting the distributor and the spark coil, preferably near the distributor end. It may also be necessary to install suppressors at each spark plug, or to replace the plugs with resistor-type spark plugs if noise persists after installation of a distributor suppressor.

Special spark plug and distributor cables are now available which have spark suppression resistance characteristics built in. This kind of resistive cable may be used in lieu of suppressors. Whether suppressors or resistance cables are used, their use should have no effect on engine performance or gasoline mileage.

Besides radiation of impulses from the high-voltage side of the ignition system, noise is induced into the low-voltage wiring from the ignition system and is also created by the generator commutator. Capacitors installed at the generator output (not the field terminal), the ignition switch, and at the ammeter as well as at the dome-light switch will alleviate this kind of interference. Capacitors designed for this purpose are encased in a metal cylinder. The metal case connects to one plate of the capacitor, an insulated wire leads to the other. The metal mounting clamp is fastened securely to the generator frame, car frame, firewall, or body, depending upon location. The insulated wire is connected to the "hot" terminal in each case.

If noise still persists, it may be necessary to install wheel static suppressors and bonding between the engine and the frame using a copper braid strap. Bonding of the frame to the body, the tail pipe to the muffler, and the hood to the body may also further suppress noise.

There is nothing that can be done about ignition noise picked up by a class D set from nearby vehicles. However, the better the antenna system, the less the interference, since stronger signals will tend to offset ignition noise and permit the receiver to be operated at lower gain settings. If the receiver employs a.v.c., the receiver gain will be automatically reduced as signal strength increases.

If the receiver has a suitable noise limiter, then the effects of ignition or other noises should be minimized.

Mounting

Many of the class D sets are provided with mounting brackets to facilitate under-dash mounting. Installation is seldom an involved project and is well within the capabilities of the do-it-yourselfer. In many cases, no permanent installation or mounting is required. Figs. 7-4 and 7-5 show some typical installations.

Testing

After the equipment is installed, the wiring should be checked. Some sets might be damaged if connected to the battery in reverse polarity. (In some cars the positive battery terminal is grounded; the negative is grounded in others.)

Class D sets are generally delivered ready-to-go. However, vibration and shock encountered in shipment as well as exposure to severe temperature changes might cause sufficient shift in tuning adjustments to require tune-up by a technically competent and licensed technician in order to get all the performance that was originally built into the equipment.

To test communicating range, it is customary for the operator of one station to transmit, calling out first number "one," while

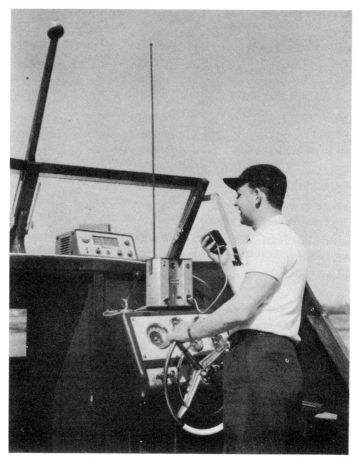

Fig. 7–4. This RCA portable Class D set requires no permanent installation when used on a boat. The set is placed on top of the dashboard here with its telescoping whip antenna extended. (*Courtesy: RCA Corporation.*)

the other station listens. The second station broadcasts "two" while the first listens, and so on. By using short transmissions, less air time is consumed. It is imperative that all stations identify themselves at the start and end of a test. It is even more important that tests not be made when the channel is in use.

If the range proves to be shorter than expected, the equipment may not be correctly tuned or installed or the manufacturer's in-

Fig. 7–5.   The "Poly-Comm," a four-channel class D unit, takes up little space under the dash. (*Photo by Jacques Saphier.*)

structions are not being followed. Allowance must be made for such factors as shielding effect of trees, hills, and buildings as well as the presence of ignition noise from other vehicles. Range will usually be slightly greater in winter when there is less foliage. With experience, the user will know what he can and cannot do with his equipment. Frequently, a more efficient antenna system will add the extra amount of range desired.

Base and Fixed Station Installation

Because of the simplicity and compactness of Class D equipment, installation of the base station or fixed station is usually very simple. The Citizens Radio unit may be installed on a desk, table, shelf, or any flat surface. It must have adequate ventilation to prevent overheating. Also, its frequency stability will be improved by installing it where the ambient temperature will remain fairly constant.

The metal chassis or cabinet of the equipment should be grounded through the shortest possible length of wire to a ground rod driven into the earth in damp soil or to a cold-water pipe or tap. This ground wire may improve performance as well as provide lightning protection. Since the outer conductor of the coaxial cable leading to the antenna is connected to the ground plane radials (when a ground plane antenna is used), and often to the antenna mounting assembly, the coaxial cable and the added ground wire provide a good circuit to ground. It is better yet to run a solid copper or aluminum wire (No. 10 to No. 6) from the antenna mounting assembly direct to a good ground. If the radio unit does not employ a power transformer, grounding of the set might cause a short circuit. In such a case insert a .01-uf. capacitor in series with the ground wire.

For the city dweller who lives in an apartment house, the installation of an antenna for a Citizens Radio unit may pose a problem. Fig. 7-6 shows some locations and mounting arrangements that may be used. In most cases, the best results are obtained with the antenna at the greatest effective elevation. However, where the user is on one of the lower floors and a very long transmission line is required to feed a roof antenna, a window-mounted dipole might work out better. It is a good idea to experiment with different locations in order to determine which is best.

Boat Installation

Although the Coast Guard, as a matter of policy, does not monitor Citizens Band channels, in spite of public interest and demand, thousands of pleasure craft and commercial vessels use Citizens Band radio for ship-to-ship and private ship-to-shore communications are well as for emergency purposes. Channel 13 has been unofficially adopted as the marine calling channel and is monitored by members of the Volunteer Marine Watch.

While almost any mobile Citizens Radio unit can be readily mounted even on small vessels, troubles are encountered on power boats which do not affect vehicular installations. First of all, the radio unit should be installed where it will receive adequate ventilation, yet be protected from direct sun rays and water spray.

The radio unit and its antenna should not be near the engine

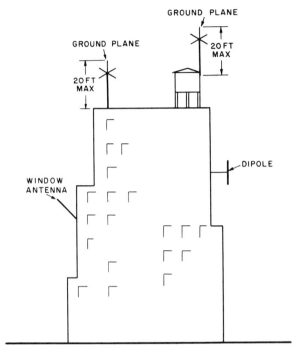

Fig. 7–6. Typical antenna locations for the apartment-house dweller's Citizens Radio station.

which is a source of radio noise interference. When the vessel has a 12-volt battery, the radio unit can be operated directly from the battery through short, heavy gauge insulated copper wire, properly fused to avoid fire hazards. The antenna transmission line should be as short as practical and should not be run near the engine nor near electric wiring.

When the vessel's electric power system delivers other than 6 or 12 volts d.c., an inverter or converter is required. A d.c. to a.c. inverter is used when the source is d.c. and the radio unit is of the a.c. operated type. Or, a 12-volt d.c. operated radio unit can be used when an appropriate converter is used for reducing the voltage of a d.c. source, or when a d.c. to a.c. inverter and an a.c. adaptor are used. In the latter case, the required 12 volts d.c. is derived from the adaptor which operates from an a.c. source.

8 ～～～～

MAINTAINING THE CITIZENS RADIO

There are many maintenance functions which can be performed by the nontechnically trained Citizens Radio station owner. There are also some which require the attention of a qualified technician and others which can be performed only by a suitably licensed operator. Maintenance, for the sake of this discussion, includes tuning, changing frequencies, preventive techniques, troubleshooting, and repair.

Changing Transmitting Frequencies

To change transmitter operating frequency in a single-channel unit, it is necessary to replace the crystal with one of appropriate frequency and to retune the transmitter to the new frequency. A crystal designed for use with the particular transmitter should be used. The mere fact that a crystal is labeled as being ground to the appropriate frequency is not assurance that it is suitable. There may be differences in the capacity of its holder with relation to the crystal element as well as other subtle differences which can cause the transmitter to operate on a frequency somewhat removed from that marked on the crystal itself. The actual operating frequency may not then be within the narrow frequency tolerance (.005 per cent) prescribed by the FCC for class D use.

In multichannel transmitters, new crystals are required only for those channels which are to be altered. Better results will be obtained if all the channels are close to each other in frequency, i.e., channels 1, 2, 3, and 4 or 16, 17, 18, and 19. If a transmitter is set up to operate on channels 1, 8, 16, and 23, for instance, the frequency spread may be so great that it may be impossible to tune the transmitter so that the same output power will not be delivered on all channels.

116

Since it is unlikely that all of the many manufacturers who are now building Citizens Radio equipment will find it profitable to stay in the business, there are apt to be some orphan sets in use in the future. While crystals may no longer be available from the original equipment manufacturer, suitable equivalents will be obtainable from any of several crystal manufacturers. When ordering crystals from other than the maker (or his dealer) of the Citizens Radio unit, it is important to specify operating frequency and tolerance as well as make, model, and serial number of the unit in which the crystals are to be used. In addition, if available, a copy of the schematic diagram should accompany the order.

Changing Receiver Frequencies

New crystals are generally required when you want to change the operating frequency of crystal controlled fixed-tuned receivers. Since superregenerative receivers or continuously tunable superhets do not employ crystals, it is necessary only to retune the receiver. In a transceiver like the RCA "Radio-Phone," the receiver and the transmitter are retuned simultaneously. (A new crystal is required for the transmitter only.)

When a new crystal is installed in a single-channel receiver, the receiver r.f. and mixer circuits should be realigned to the new frequency. The second oscillator crystal in dual-conversion receivers does *not* have to be changed. It remains the same for all operating frequencies.

In multichannel receivers, frequencies are also changed by replacing crystals and retuning the r.f. and mixer circuits for optimum operation on all channels. However, in the Philmore TC-11, which employs a superregenerative receiver, each of its three fixed-tuned receiving channels may be retuned to a different channel. The applicable instruction book usually outlines specific tuning procedures.

The operating frequency of a single-channel, single-conversion receiver can be changed by replacement of the crystal and retuning the r.f. and mixer circuits to the new frequency. However, when changing to an adjacent channel (above or below) , the original crystal may be left in the set and the i.f. transformers may be retuned 10 KH$_z$ higher or lower than the frequency to which they were originally tuned. If the i.f. amplifier is tuned to 1600 KH$_z$, for example, and a crystal for operation of the receiver on 27.115 MH$_z$ is in the set, reception on 27.125 MH$_z$ is possible by retuning the i.f. transformers to 1610 KH$_z$ and the r.f. and mixer circuits to 27.125 MH$_z$. Or to set up the receiver for 27.105 MH$_z$, the i.f. transformers are tuned to 1590 KH$_z$ and the r.f. and mixer circuits to 27.105 MH$_z$. Although this procedure may not be satisfactory for all receivers, it seems worth trying in order to save the cost of a new crystal. A suitable calibrated signal generator should be available for use as a frequency standard.

Similar receiver frequency changes may be made in dual-conversion receivers, but it is a slightly more complex process. If, for example, the original operating frequency is 27.115 MH$_z$ and operation on 27.125 MH$_z$ is desired, the i.f. amplifier may be retuned from 455 KH$_z$ (if that is the i.f.) to 465 KH$_z$. The input of the second mixer is retuned to 6.01 MH$_z$ (if the first i.f. is 6 MH$_z$) and the r.f. and first mixer are retuned to 27.125 MH$_z$. The 27.125-MH$_z$ incoming signal, when mixed with the 21.115-MH$_z$ oscillator frequency, will yield a 6.01-MH$_z$ beat. At the second mixer, the 6.01-MH$_z$ signal is mixed with the 6.455-MH$_z$ signal from the second oscillator, yielding a 465-KH$_z$ beat. Similar techniques may be used for shifting from any channel to an adjacent channel above or below the original frequency. However, it is possible that the i.f. transformers may not be tunable over a sufficiently wide band, or that sensitivity may not be as good if the i.f. transformers are detuned from their intended frequency.

The first local oscillator in the Commaire ED-27 (Vocaline) is crystal controlled and the second local oscillator is tunable (internal adjustment). When changing receiving frequency, the crystal is not replaced. Instead, the second oscillator is retuned Thus, only one crystal is required for reception on any channel in the band.

Receiver Alignment

The instruction books normally furnished with Citizens Radio equipment ordinarily give specific instructions on how to align the receiver's tuned circuits. The procedures are, in general, the same for all AM superheterodyne receivers.

To align a receiver properly, a signal generator and a vacuum-tube voltmeter (v.t.v.m.) are employed. The signal generator may be of almost any type, whether designed for servicing home radios or for the laboratory, so long as it will tune between about 400 KH$_z$ and 28 MH$_z$. If it will tune to 14 MH$_z$, it is likely that its second harmonic will be strong enough to make the instrument suitable for use at 28 MH$_z$. There are many instruments on the market at prices ranging from under $30 (in kit form) to $1,000 or more for extremely accurate lab-type units.

The v.t.v.m. may be of almost any make or type as long as it will measure d.c. voltage. These are available from around $25 in kit form to several hundred dollars or more for laboratory instruments. For this purpose, the accuracy of calibration of the meter is not important. All we are looking for is a relative indication of output.

The v.t.v.m. is connected between the a.v.c. bus and the chassis. The signal-generator output is connected through a blocking capacitor (say .01 mf. or whatever value is suggested by the manufacturer) to the grid of the second mixer tube (first mixer in a single-conversion superheterodyne) and the cabinet of the signal generator is grounded to the receiver chassis. See Fig. 8-1. The first and second oscillator crystals are removed. The signal generator is tuned to the intermediate frequency (for example, 455 KH$_z$) and the signal generator output is turned down as low as possible just so a readable voltage appears on the a.v.c. bus.

Starting with the secondary of the detector i.f. transformer and working back toward the mixer, each i.f. transformer trimmer is tuned for maximum indication on the v.t.v.m. As the voltage reading increases with the gain improvements made, the signal generator output should be backed off to prevent overloading any of the tubes.

After completing the i.f. alignment, the second oscillator crystal is placed back into its socket and the signal-generator output is connected (through a capacitor) to the grid of the first mixer. With the signal generator tuned to the second mixer input frequency (say, 6 MH$_z$ or 8 MH$_z$), the second mixer input circuits are tuned for maximum v.t.v.m. indication. (This, of course, is required only for double-conversion receivers.)

With the first oscillator crystal (or crystals) back in the socket,

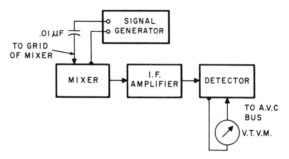

Fig. 8–1. The detector and i.f. amplifier should be aligned first.

the signal-generator output is connected through a 51-ohm carbon resistor to the antenna input terminal or socket. The signal generator is set to the operating frequency or one-half the operating frequency if the signal generator will not tune to 28 MH$_z$. If the operating frequency is 27.075 MH$_z$, the signal generator is set to that frequency or 13.5375 MH$_z$. With the signal-generator output turned very low, just enough to get an indication on the v.t.v.m., the mixer input circuit and then the r.f. amplifier circuits are tuned for maximum meter indication.

When an accurate signal generator is not available, another class D Citizens Radio transmitter operated on a dummy antenna in another room can be used as the signal source for accurately aligning the antenna, r.f., and the mixer stages (see Fig. 8-2) .

While alignment is not a difficult chore for the expert, it will be difficult for one with very little or no electronic equipment servicing experience. It has been stated that the signal generator should be set to a certain frequency, but even if the instrument's tuning dial indicates that it is set to that frequency, this may not be actually so. A signal generator whose calibration accuracy can be relied upon is an expensive device. A low-priced instrument, however, will suffice if used correctly since the primary objective is to get a usable radio signal. It is important that the signal be at the right frequency.

To get an idea of the importance of frequency calibration, consider this. If the signal-generator frequency calibration is off only 1 per cent, it will be off by 4.55 KH$_z$ when tuned to 455 KH$_z$

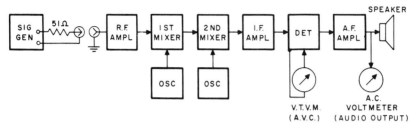

Fig. 8–2. Front-end alignment is made by applying a weak signal at the antenna connector; by measuring audio output voltage, over-all sensitivity of receiver can be determined.

and by 271 KH$_z$ when thought to be set at 27.115MH$_z$. That would put the signal some twenty-seven channel spacings away. The inaccuracy at the i.f. frequency then may not be too serious, but it cannot be tolerated at the incoming r.f. frequency.

Unless someone has tampered with the i.f. transformer adjustments, chances are that the i.f. amplifier is tuned very close to the right frequency. So, when making i.f. tuning adjustments, the signal generator tuning dial is tuned back and forth in the general area of the receiver's intermediate frequency. When the v.t.v.m. swings upward, the signal generator should then be tuned carefully until the meter reads maximum and left there with the expectation that this is the right frequency.

Once the i.f. amplifiers have been tuned, the rest of the tuning can be done without the signal generator, using an off-the-air signal instead and with the receiver connected to an antenna. The second mixer input, first mixer, and r.f. circuits can then be tuned for maximum meter indication. The problem encountered when using an off-the-air signal is that such signals don't stay on long enough at a time to permit making fine adjustments. And, if another station is asked to hold its press-to-talk button down while the adjustments are made, the operator of the other station will be in violation of the FCC rule that prohibits superfluous communications and will be violating the rules of common courtesy since use of the channel by others will be impaired.

While an expert can sometimes tune a receiver using an electric razor as a signal generator and can diagnose troubles using a screwdriver or a wet finger as a voltmeter, the nonexpert may find that attempting the alignment of a superheterodyne receiver without adequate equipment and sufficient know-how will wind up by having to have the work undone by an expert. Three decades ago, almost anyone could fix a model A engine, but few motorists today would dare tamper with the engine of a modern high-powered car.

Transmitter Tuning

Initial Citizens Radio transmitter adjustments should be made only when a dummy antenna is used to prevent radiation. Final tuning adjustments, however, can be made only by a licensed operator with an antenna connected. All test transmissions should be kept as short as possible when making on-the-air adjustments, to avoid causing interference to others.

Tuning a transmitter is a simple chore. The procedures will vary among various types and makes of equipment. To tune a transmitter, an expert might be able to do it with a flashlight or neon bulb and a screwdriver. However, he, as well as the novice, can do it better with the proper instruments.

Transmitter adjustments should *not* be made with antenna connected, except by a licensed operator. In lieu of an antenna, a dummy load may be connected. A dummy load may consist of ten 510-ohm carbon resistors connected in parallel across the terminals of a plug that mates with the transmitter's antenna receptacle (Fig. 8-3). Or it may be a No. 40 or No. 47 pilot lamp. Since these lamps are rated at only 1 watt, they may burn out. It would be better to connect four or six of these lamps in series-parallel. See Fig. 8-4. Or, an r.f. wattmeter of the termination type may be used as a dummy load as well as for measuring the power output of the transmitter.

The antenna and its transmission line contain capacitance, inductance, and resistance so it would appear that the dummy load should be more complex than a mere resistance. However, most equipment is designed to work into resonant antennas with a prop-erly matched transmission line. Under these conditions it should be possible to simulate a ground-plane or other standard type of antenna with a pure resistance of around 50 ohms or to simulate an ordinary dipole antenna with a pure resistance of around 70 ohms.

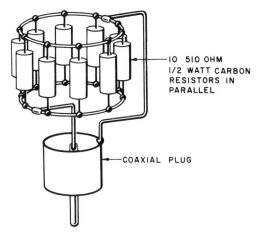

Fig. 8–3. Dummy antenna.

It is standard practice to use a noninductive resistance as a dummy load. This means that a carbon or composition-type resistor, not a wire-wound type, or bank of carbon resistors (to handle about 5 or 6 watts) should be used. The trouble with a lamp as a dummy load is that its resistance when cold or glowing dimly is different from its resistance when it glows at normal brilliance. It therefore becomes a variable dummy load and is thus not as suitable as a fixed resistor.

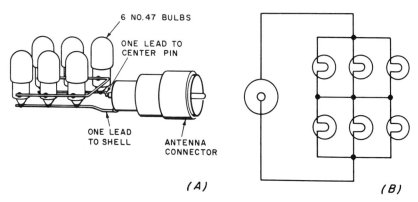

Fig. 8–4. A handy transmitter antenna dummy load can be made up from six No. 47 pilot lamps and an antenna conductor. Solder bases of bulbs together. Connect short, heavy lead from center contacts to three lamps to center of coax plug. Connect center contacts of the three other lamps to shell of plug.

Since a class D transmitter is a two- or a three-stage affair, tuning of the r.f. circuits is simple and has been kept that way by most of the equipment manufacturers. One manufacturer suggests that an r.f. wattmeter be plugged into the antenna outlet. The three transmitter tuning adjustments are then made for maximum reading on the meter and one is backed off just a bit to insure better stability. In some cases tuning is accomplished by metering the grid currents of the various stages and making adjustments for plate-current minimum or near-minimum readings. Under these conditions the antenna adjustment, if any, is made to cause an increase in r.f. power-amplifier current reading.

To tune a specific transmitter, the instructions of the manufacturer should be followed. While even an expert may feel he knows a better way, the engineers who designed the equipment may have had very valid reasons for recommending their way. Anything to the contrary could cause the transmitter to operate in a manner which would be in violation of FCC rules.

Troubleshooting

If the equipment does not operate at all, the first thing to check is the availability of power. This means power at the house current outlet, the vehicle battery, as well as equipment fuses. In the case of vehicular installations where an a.c./d.c. converter is used for operation of an a.c-type unit, the output of the converter should be checked with a voltmeter or one of those handy neon light testers that are available at most hardware stores.

Nonoperation of a direct battery operated unit casts suspicion on the vibrator if one is used. Vibrator operation can be checked by listening closely to note if it is buzzing. If a rectifier tube is used in the equipment, its failure could prevent the radiotelephone from operating.

The ability to receive without being able to transmit obviously indicates transmitter trouble. It is possible that the transmitter is putting out an r.f. signal but is not being modulated. This can be determined by touching the glass bulb of a neon lamp or one end of a small 15-watt fluorescent lamp to the antenna (Fig. 8-5). If the lamp glows, the transmitter is putting out an r.f. signal. (*Note:* This may not always work if a fluorescent lamp is used, since the lamp may so load down the transmitter as to stop its operation. But in any case, the method is worth trying.) When talking loudly into the microphone, the brilliance of the lamp should vary. If it does not, there is no modulation. Lack of modulation could be caused by a defective microphone, a bad connection, a defective

Fig. 8–5. A 15-watt fluorescent lamp or neon lamp held close to the plug-in whip antenna will usually glow if the transmitter is functioning properly. (*Photo by Jacques Saphier.*)

Fig. 8–6. Transmitter operation can be checked with a simple crystal set consisting of a foot of wire wound into a coil, a crystal diode, and a pair of headphones. (*Photo by Jacques Saphier.*)

tube, or component failure. Lack of an r.f. signal may be caused by a defective crystal, tube, or component or a dirty relay contact.

Another way to check the transmitter is to take a foot-long piece of bell or hook-up wire and coil it up. The coil is connected in series with a crystal diode (a 1N34 may be used) and a pair of headphones as shown in Fig. 8-6. With the plug-in antenna inside the coil of wire, sounds picked up by the microphone with the transmitter turned on, should be heard in the earphones.

Receiver operation can be checked quickly. If there is a squelch control, noise should be heard when the squelch control is moved to the fully unsquelched position. If noises but no signals are heard, the trouble could be in the antenna system. Another quick way to check the receiver is to hold a pocket-sized transistor radio next to the plug-in whip antenna. As the dial of the portable receiver is tuned slowly, a rushing sound should be heard at the point where a harmonic of the local oscillator in the pocket radio is at the Citizens Radio receiver's operating frequency (see Fig. 8-7).

A burned-out tube can usually be located by noting the absence of heater glow in the tube's envelope. In bright light it is often difficult to see the glow of the tube heater because of the coating inside of the glass envelope. If the set has been turned on for some time, the tubes should feel warm to the touch. A cold tube should be suspected as being defective.

In the absence of a tube tester, new tubes may be tried one at a time, always putting the original tube back in its socket if a new one does not cure the trouble. The tubes can be tested by an electronics technician at almost any radio-TV service shop. The fact that a tube passes muster on a tube tester (except a laboratory-grade instrument that simulates the circuit conditions found in the Citizens Radio unit) does not necessarily mean that the tube will function in a high-frequency transmitter or receiver.

Preventive Maintenance

Like an automobile or a television set, better performance and longer equipment life can be obtained from a Citizens Radio unit if it is given proper preventive maintenance. The first requisite of preventive maintenance is keeping the equipment clean. Dust and dirt should be wiped off or blown out. Dust, dirt, and oil film can retard adequate cooling of the parts and can lead to early equipment failure.

Tubes and vibrators have a limited life. They are usually rated at 1,000 hours of actual operating life. Some may fail within the first 200 hours of use while some radio tubes placed in service 30 years ago are still functioning. Replacement of tubes at regular intervals is not considered an unreasonable maintenance expense. A new tube, however, may fail after only a few hours of use. That is why manufacturers often provide warranty replacements.

Fig. 8–7. A pocket transister radio can be used as a signal generator to check receiver operation. A harmonic of its local oscillator is picked up by the receiver if the receiver is operative. (*Courtesy: Lafayette Radio.*)

Frequency Check

Transmitter frequencies should be checked at regular intervals to make sure that the transmitter is operating within the proper frequency tolerance and that it conforms with the other FCC requirements. The FCC may require a Citizens Radio licensee to have such measurements made when a transmitter is suspected of improper operation. The frequency measurement may be made by an unlicensed person if the FCC accepts him as competent to do so.

A class D Citizens Radio transmitter is required to keep its operating frequency within .005 per cent of any of the twenty-three class D channels. To measure frequency accurately enough, the measuring instrument should be accurate to at least .0025 per cent, that is, it must be twice as accurate as the transmitter must be. An instrument that will measure the frequency that closely is an inexpensive device. Cushman, Lampkin, Singer, Marconi, International, and Hewlett-Packard are mong the firms that manufacture frequency meters or electronic counters suitable for this purpose.

In the absence of suitable test instruments, the Citizens Radio may be taken to a two-way radio maintenance shop where suitable equipment and trained personnel are available.

Modulation Measurement

Since most class D transmitters cannot achieve, but only approach, 100 per cent modulation, there is little need for measurement of modulation except to determine if it is high enough. Low modulation level will cause a loss in the effectiveness of a transmitter. To the listener operating a distant receiver, the modulation will appear not to "fill up" the carrier completely. The rush of the carrier will be closely audible in the background. On the other hand, if there is overmodulation the signal will sound badly distorted.

Elaborate modulation-measuring instruments are available for checking modulation percentage. It is also possible to use an ordinary oscilloscope for such measurements. Information on the proper technique to use is discussed in standard texts.

9 ~~~~~~~~

HOW TO USE CITIZENS RADIO

A Citizens Radio transmitter radiates a signal that can serve a useful purpose. It can also cause harmful interference to others. It could serve as a guide post for friendly or enemy aircraft, or it could attract an enemy missile. When improperly used, a Citizens Radio can become an instrument of abuse. Since a Citizens Radio station is used primarily for conveying the human voice from one point to another over a *public* communications highway, it must be used discreetly.

It is necessary that all radio stations identify themselves. Unidentified stations can be traced down and located. If found to be unlicensed, their operators are liable to prosecution. Licensed stations failing to identify themselves are subject to disciplinary action.

A Citizens Radio station is required to transmit its assigned call letters at the beginning and end of all communications and an exchange of communications should be no longer than 5 minutes in duration.

In mobile radio, including Citizens Radio, an exchange of communications consists of one or more short transmissions by each of two intercommunicating stations. Unlike radio amateurs, who often transmit long monologues each way, mobile radio is used for rapid exchanges of words in two directions. By being brief, more people can use the same channel. Many users employ a code for transmitting intelligence quickly, see Tables 9-1 and 9-2.

Language Of the CBer

Citizens radio operators have become popularly known as "CBers," short for "citizens banders." They, like radio amateurs (hams) , have developed some new words and expressions they use

130

Table 9–1 Sample numbered code used by trucking firms which Citizens Radio users could adopt

Code 1 What is your location?	Code 7 Do you have room for freight?
Code 2 I am at	Code 8 I have a pickup for you.
Code 3 Is loading dock crowded?	Code 9 Acknowledgment (OK).
Code 4 Loading dock crowded. Expect long wait.	Code 10 Call me by telephone.
Code 5 Even though dock is crowded make your pickup (or delivery).	Code 11 I am leaving my truck.
	Code 12 I am in my truck.
Code 6 Proceed to your next pickup (or delivery).	Code 13 Stand by (I'll call you back).

Table 9–2 10-Code

The 10-code is widely used by CBers and public safety officers. The most popular abbreviations are listed here.

10–1	Receiving poorly	10–23	Stand by
10–2	Receiving well	10–24	Have you finished?
10–3	Stop transmitting	10–25	Do you have contact with . . . . ?
10–4	OK or acknowledged		
10–5	Relay this message	10–30	Does not conform with rules
10–6	Busy, stand by	10–33	Emergency traffic
10–7	Leaving the air	10–35	Confidential information
10–8	Back on the air, standing by	10–36	Correct time
10–9	Repeat message	10–54	Accident
10–10	Transmission completed, standing by	10–55	Tow truck needed
		10–56	Ambulance needed
10–11	Speak more slowly	10–82	Reserve room for . . . .
10–13	Advise weather and road conditions	10–88	What is phone number of . . . . ?
10–19	Return to base	10–89	Repairman needed
10–20	What is your location?	10–90	Repairman will arrive at . . . .
10–21	Call. . . . . . . by telephone		
10–22	Report in person to	10–99	Unable to receive you

on the air. Some of this CB language below is reprinted with permission from CB Magazine.

AF	Audio frequency, signals that are audible (below 20 KHz)
AGC	Automatic gain control circuit used in receivers which reduces gain as the intercepted radio signal level increases, and vice versa.
Amateur	A person licensed in the Amateur Radio Service (see Ham).

ANL | Automatic noise limiter.
Antenna Gain | A figure of merit of an antenna with respect to a dipole or isotropic antenna. If an antenna has 3 db gain, the effective radiated power (ERP) of the transmitter is doubled.
AVC | Automatic volume control circuit used in receivers which varies gain so as to maintain constant audio output level.
Antenna Tester | See SWR meter
Bangers and Mash | Sausages and mashed potatoes.
Beam | A type of antenna which is highly directional, like a spot light.
Bottle | Slang for tube.
CB | Citizens band.
CBL Card | Same as QSL card but used by CBers only.
Channel | A specified radio transmitting frequency.
Class A | A class of CB station license authorizing operation on an assigned channel in the 460-470 MHz band.
Class B | A class of CB station for which new licenses will no longer be granted.
Class C | A CB station license authorizing transmission of radio control signals.
Class D | A CB station license authorizing operation on any of the 23 available channels in "the" citizens band (27-MHz band).
Coax | Coaxial cable.
Compression Amplifier | See modulation booster.
CRS | Citizens Radio Service.
Crystal | A piece of quartz whose physical dimensions determine the frequency at which it will function as a resonant circuit.
Decibel (db) | A quantitative unit of measure. Doubling power is equal to 3 db. Doubling voltage is a 6 db increase.
Detector | A circuit in a receiver which extracts the audio signal (voice) from the inaudible radio signal.
Diode | A two-element tube (with plate and cathode) or a semiconductor device which passes current readily in one direction but blocks current flow in the opposite direction. Semiconductor diodes are commonly used in CB transceivers as rectifiers, detectors and gates.
D.O.T. | Department of Transport, Canadian equivalent of the FCC.
DX | Long distance.
EAE | Effective antenna elevation, height with respect to surroundings, not necessarily height above ground.
Eighty-eight (88) | Love and Kisses.
Eleven Meter Band | The 27-MHz citizens band, formerly known as the 11-meter amateur band.

ERP	Effective radiated power.
Frequency	The pitch of a sound or radio signal which differentiates it from another.
Frequency Stability	The precision with which a frequency is maintained at its intended value.
Frequency Tolerance	For a Class D CB transmitter, the "tolerance" (accuracy) and the stability of the transmitting frequency should be within ±0.005% of the designated channel frequency.
Ground Plane	Part of an antenna or antenna system (such as car roof). Also refers to a ground plane antenna.
Ground Wave	A radio signal traveling along the earth's surface.
GRS	General Radio Service, Canadian equivalent of Citizens Radio Service.
Handie-Talkie	A copyrighted trade mark used correctly only when referring to a Motorola product.
Ham	An amateur radio operator, one who can lawfully engage in radio transmission as a hobby.
HELP	Highway Emergency Locating Plan, sponsored by the Automobile Manufacturers Association.
HF	High frequency, the 3–30 MHz portion of the radio spectrum in which "the" citizens band is located.
Hybrid	An electronic device employing both tubes and transistors.
Hz	Hertz, meaning cycles per second.
IF Amplifier	Intermediate frequency amplifier. The section of a receiver between the mixer and the detector which provides most of the gain and selectivity.
KHz	KiloHertz, meaning kilocycles or thousands of cycles per second.
Lid	An inept radio operator, such as a deliberate rule violator or one who doesn't know any better.
MHz	MegaHertz, meaning megacycles or millions of cycles per second.
Microvolt (uv)	Millionth of a volt.
Mike	Microphone
Modulation Booster	A device or built-in circuit in a CB transceiver which adds gain to a microphone circuit to make it more sensitive, but which automatically limits output to prevent over-modulation.
Megacycle (mc, mc/s)	Obsolete term for millions of cycles per second, now MegaHertz.
Mubble Fubbles	In low spirits.
Muck Around	Having an ad lib bash at something.
Noise Blanker	See noise limiter. Similar, but chops holes in signal path ahead of the detector.
Noise Limiter	A circuit which reduces impulse type noise in a CB receiver by chopping holes in the audio signal path.
OM	Old man.
Oscillator	An electronic generator of AC signals (including RF). The source of the radio signal of a CB transmitter.

Out	Radio operator's term for "this communications exchange is finished."
Part 15	That part of FCC Rules and Regulations which covers unlicensed low power transmitters.
"S" Meter	A meter which indicates the level of an intercepted radio signal and which is calibrated in "S" units (1–9).
Scofflaw	Rule violator.
Semiconductor	A solid state device such as a diode or transistor.
Seventy-three (73)	Best regards (73, not 73's).
Skip	A radio signal from a distant radio station reflected by the ionosphere.
Sky Hook	Antenna
Sky Wire	Antenna
S/N	Signal-to-noise ratio.
S + N/N	Ratio of signal plus noise to noise.
Solid State	An electronic device or circuit employing no tubes.
Squelch	An electronic circuit in a receiver which mutes the loudspeaker except when a radio signal is intercepted (cuts out noise between intercepted transmissions).
Speaker	Loudspeaker.
Superhet	Superheterodyne circuit, now commonly used in CB transceivers because of its high sensitivity and selectivity.
SWR	Standing wave ratio (short for VSWR).
SWR Meter	A measuring device connected between the antenna transmission line and the transceiver for measuring VSWR.
Synthesizer	A device for crystal controlling a large number of frequencies with a few crystals.
Tank	Tuned circuit of a transmitter.
Ten-code	Abbreviations originally used by police and other land mobile radio users, now widely used by CBers.
Tone Squelch	A squelch circuit which keeps the speaker muted until a radio signal is intercepted which is modulated by a tone at a specific frequency or a specific coded tone combination.
T-R Switch	Transmit-receive control switch.
Transistor	A solid state semiconductor valve used mainly as an amplifier.
Transistorized	An electronic device employing transistors, but not necessarily in all circuits.
Tube	A thermionic valve.
TVI	Television interference as caused "by" CB transmitters.
Type Acceptance	When a CB transceiver has been "type accepted," it means that the manufacturer has proved to the FCC that it meets FCC technical standards. Proposed CB rules changes (which might be in effect when this is printed) will require all new CB transceivers to be type accepted in order to be licensable.
UHF	Ultrahigh frequency, the 300–3000 MHz portion of the radio spectrum in which "that other" citizens band (the original) is located.

VAC	Volts, alternating current.
VDC	Volts, direct current.
Vibrator	A device used in some CB transceiver power supplies for converting DC into AC. It is electro-mechanical, employing moving parts and contacts, and is subject to wear.
VSWR	Voltage standing wave ratio, a term used to denote the efficiency of an antenna system from the standpoint of impedance matching. A VSWR of 1:1 is ideal, but not practical. Usually, the lower the VSWR the better since more of the available transmitter power is being fed into the antenna.
XYL	Wife.
YL	Young lady.

FCC Limits On Use Of Citizens Radio

The use of a Citizens Radio station is limited by the FCC to the following:

1 Communication with other Citizens Radio stations on specified channels only.

2 The licensee may not provide radio communications service to any person.

3 Communications shall be limited to the *minimum* practicable transmission time.

However, during a period of emergency in which normal communications facilities are disrupted, a Citizens Radio station may be utilized for emergency communications in violation of items 1 and 3 above. The emergency conditions considered grave enough include hurricane, floods, earthquakes, or enemy attacks.

As soon as possible after starting such emergency use of a Citizens Radio station, FCC headquarters in Washington, or the engineer in charge of the FCC field office in the applicable radio district concerned, must be notified. The notice must state the nature of the emergency and how the station is being used. As soon as the emergency is over, the use of the station for communication with other than Citizens Radio stations must be discontinued and the FCC must be so notified.

Citizens Radio stations may also participate in civil defense activities, on a voluntary basis, provided that operation of the station will not conflict with normal communications and only when such communications are conducted under the direction of civil defense authorities. The FCC should be notified, in advance if possible, of such activities, and the FCC has the authority to ban such operation.

A Citizens Radio station is specifically prohibited from:

1 Communicating with radio stations in any other radio service (amateur, railroad, public safety, industrial, etc.), except in emergencies.

2 Exacting a fee or accepting compensation for radio communications services provided.

3 Transmitting program material of any kind (music, news, etc.).

4 Being used as a wireless microphone. (Public address broadcasting of signals transmitted by a Citizens radio-telephone.)

5 Being used for any unlawful purpose.

6 Transmission of profane or obscene communications.

Keep Transmission Brief

A Citizens Radio station is *not* intended to be a substitute for a ham station. It is not intended for the transmission of long personal conversations. Prearranged numbered code signals (spoken) might be used to keep on-the-air time to a minimum. (Refer to Tables 9-1 and 9-2.) Transmission of a CQ (calling any station) to alert any station that might be listening is contrary to the purpose for which the Citizens Radio Service was established. However, in the case of boats seeking navigational or safety information or in need of assistance, transmission of a CQ call to determine if any other vessels capable of providing information or aid are in the vicinity seems to be a reasonable act, not in violation of basic precepts.

Here is what a typical exchange of communications between two Citizens Radio stations sounds like:

Station 1: "This is KOD-1939, unit one calling mobile unit two. Over."

Station 2: "This is KOD-1939, unit two returning your call. Over."

Station 1: "Where are you? Over."

Station 2: "I'm very close to buoy No. 2 out in the channel. Over."

    Station 1: "Please come right in and tie up at pier No. 3. Over."

    Station 2: "OK. I'll be right in in around 20 minutes. Anything else? Over."

    Station 1: "That's all. KOD-1939, unit one is off."

    Station 2: "KOD-1939, unit two is off."

Station License

A radio station license must be obtained before a Citizens Radio transmitter can be put on the air. This does not mean that the transmitter can be put on the air immediately after filing the license application. At least 3 weeks should be allowed for license processing time. The license document, or a telegram from the FCC with the statement that the license has been granted, must be on hand.

A single license usually covers authority for a complete system. The same license may cover a number of mobile stations operated in the same system or general geographical area.

An identification card must be affixed to every transmitter except where the actual license or photostatic copy of the license is posted. These cards (FCC form 452-C, revised) are available from the FCC. They must be properly executed noting (1) the name of the station licensee, (2) assigned station call letters, (3) exact location(s) where permanent station records are maintained and (4) frequency(ies) to which the transmitter is tuned. (5) The card must also bear the signature of the licensee.

The actual station license document must be posted at the principal base or fixed station with photostatic copies posted at all other fixed or base stations covered by the same license.

Applying For a License

License applications are made by completing and filing FCC form 505 with the Federal Communications Commission, Gettysburg, Pa. The form consists of a number of sheets of paper of which one is a work sheet to be retained by the applicant.

A separate FCC form 505 must be filed for each group of class D units, regardless of how many are in each group, which are to be regularly operated in separate geographical areas. For example, two separate license applications must be filed to operate a group of class D units in Seattle and another group in San Francisco, even if they are all owned and controlled by the same applicant.

An instruction sheet is provided with FCC form 505 which gives detailed instructions on how it should be completed. Copies of license application forms are often furnished with the equipment and are also available from the FCC.

When applying for a license for class D stations, the proposed operating frequency is not specified in the application since any licensee can operate on *any* frequency available to that specific class of station.

Any citizen of the United States over 18 years of age is eligible for a Citizens Radio station license for class D stations. A licensee may be an individual, partnership, corporation, unincorporated association, or governmental body. No alien or the representative of an alien may be granted a license. No foreign government or corporation organized under the laws of any foreign government is eligible. A license will not be granted to any corporation if any officer or director is an alien or if more than one fifth of its capital stock is owned or voted by aliens or foreign governments or their representatives. A corporation is ineligible for a radio station license if more than one fifth of its stock is owned or voted by any foreign corporation. If a corporation is controlled by any other corporation of which more than one fourth of its directors or even one officer is an alien, the FCC has the right to revoke or refuse to grant a license.

After a radio station license has been granted, it is good for five years unless stipulated otherwise on its face, or unless revoked earlier. While a radio station license is a grant of privilege, it also places responsibility on the licensee. The proper operation of the licensed radio transmitters is the responsibility of the licensee. He cannot pass the responsibility on to someone else.

A licensee who violates or appears to have violated any provision of the Communications Act of 1934, as amended, or of any applicable FCC rules or regulations is apt to be served a written notice calling attention to the facts and requesting a statement concerning the matter. The recipient is required to reply, making the answer complete in itself without reference to other documents.

The answer must state why the violations occurred and what remedial steps have been taken to prevent recurrence.

Maintenance

As explained in earlier chapters, the nontechnically trained owner of Citizens Radio equipment can perform certain limited diagnostic and maintenance functions. Even the scope of the work that can be performed by a technically competent person is limited, if such person is not the possessor of a first- or second-class commercial radio operator license. However, possession of a license is no guarantee of competence or ethical practice.

There are thousands of mobile radio service shops in all parts of the country that are staffed by persons experienced in repairing and adjusting radiotelephone equipment (Fig. 9-1). In order to render services for other landmobile radio users (fire, police, taxi, truckers, etc.), they must have adequate test equipment as well as the skill to use it. When licensed personnel of these establishments service Citizens Radio equipment, they as well as the licensee are responsible to the FCC for any errors in workmanship or judgment they might make, which might lead to violations of FCC rules. But, it such repairs are entrusted to an unlicensed person, it is the station licensee who is responsible to the FCC for proper operation of the equipment.

It is anticipated that many TV and home radio service shops will get into the mobile radio field because of the increased demand for radiotelephone maintenance service brought about by the current Citizens Radio boom. Their technicians will have to obtain licenses and the shops will have to acquire the requisite specialized test equipment.

Mobile radio maintenance shops can usually be located by consulting the yellow pages of a telephone directory. They are listed under different headings in various telephone directories. Sometimes they are listed under "Radio Communications Equipment and Service," "Mobile Radio Sales and Service," or "Radiotelephone Equipment Sales and Service." If such listings cannot be found in the telephone directory, the radio communications officer of the local police department no doubt knows where local mobile radio specialists can be reached.

Fig. 9–1. Suitable (and expensive) test equipment is required to properly maintain any kind of radio communications equipment. While a nontechnically trained owner of Citizens Radio equipment can handle a limited number of diagnostic and maintenance functions, actual repairs should be made by an expert. (*Photo by Cyril Glunk.*)

Summary Of Do's and Don't's

In mid 1959 the FCC issued a public notice announcing that over 50,000 Citizens Radio authorizations had been granted. (In mid 1969 there were over 1-million). The 1959 notice indicated some of the many uses to which Citizens Radio equipment has been made as follows:.

"The uses of Citizens Radio are as broad as the imagination of the public and the ingenuity of equipment manufacturers can devise. It is employed to page physicians and nurses in caring for the ill. It is utilized by department stores, dairies, laundries, and by other business organizations to communicate with delivery trucks. It is an aid to large industrial plants, construction projects, farms, and ranges for communicating with trucks, tractors, and other mobile units. It is used aboard pleasure and commercial craft on rivers and in harbors, and by sportsmen and explorers to maintain contact for safety and other purposes. Citizen-users, in general, benefit from the convenience of using portable two-way radio equipment for their own particular needs in places where regular communications facilities are not available and during emergencies when wire facilities break down."

But then, concerned about the growing number of violation notices to Citizens Band users, the notice went on:

"But equally important is what Citizens Radio is not. Common carrier operations are not permitted, nor may a charge be made for the use of Citizens facilities. The transmission of program material to either a broadcast station or a public address system is not permitted. The random calling of other licensees in the service is prohibited. Citizens stations may not be used as a link in a system licensed in another service."

The following edited tabulation, reprinted from *Electronics World,* summarizes some of the important do's and don't's for Citizens Band users:

You MAY use the Citizens Band for:

• Private short-distance radio communications for personal or business use, limited to the minimum practicable transmission time.

You MAY NOT use the Citizens Band for:

• A hobby-type operation in itself as opposed to its use, for example, for controlling models.
• Experimental use of radio on the air.
• Amateur operation. Calling "CQ," attempting to contact unknown Citizens Radio stations, trying to contact stations in as many states as possible is not permitted.
• DX operation. Attempting long-distance contacts with unknown stations is not permitted.
• Contacting amateurs and stations in other radio services, except in emergency.
• Recreational activity in and of itself, for pleasure to be derived from such operation.

REMEMBER:

• A station license *is* required.
• An operator's license *is not* required.
• You *may not* make any adjustments that could cause improper operation when the unit is connected to an antenna without a commercial radio operator's license.

INDEX